AIRCRAFT FUEL
METERING SYSTEMS

International Standard Book Number 0-89100-057-7
For sale by: IAP, Inc., A Hawks Industries Company
Mail To: P.O. Box 10000, Casper, WY 82602-1000
Ship To: 7383 6WN Road, Casper, WY 82604-1835
(800) 443-9250 ❖ (307) 266-3838 ❖ FAX: (307) 472-5106
WCB 05/94   Printed in the USA

IAP, Inc.
7383 6WN Road, Casper, WY 82604-1835

Printed in the United States of America

Table of Contents

Preface

This book on *Aircraft Fuel Metering Systems* is one of a series of specialized training manuals prepared for aviation maintenance personnel.

This series is part of a programmed learning course developed and produced by International Aviation Publishers (IAP), one of the largest suppliers of aviation maintenance training materials in the world. This program is part of a continuing effort to improve the quality of education for aviation mechanics throughout the world.

The purpose of each IAP training series is to provide basic information on the operation and principles of the various aircraft systems and their components.

Specific information on detailed operation procedures should be obtained from the manufacturer through his appropriate maintenance manuals, and followed in detail for the best results.

This particular manual on *Aircraft Fuel Metering Systems* includes a series of carefully prepared questions and answers to emphasize key elements of the study, and to encourage you to continually test yourself for accuracy and retention as you use this book. A multiple choice final examination is included to allow you to test your comprehension of the total material.

Some of the terminology in this book may be new to you. Throughout the text, you will find words that are defined in the Glossary at the back of the book highlighted as follows: ***glossary item***.

Acknowledgements

The validity of any program such as this is enhanced immeasurably by the cooperation shown IAP by recognized experts in the field, and by the willingness of the various manufacturers to share their literature and answer countless questions in the preparation of these programs.

We would like to mention, especially, our appreciation for help given us by:

Precision Airmotive Corporation

Division of Borg-Warner Corporation

Bendix Energy Controls Division

Teledyne Continental Motors

Shell Oil Company

Phillips Petroleum Company

If you have any questions or comments regarding this manual, or any of the many other textbooks offered by IAP simply contact: Sales Department, IAP Inc.; Mailing Address: P.O. Box 10000, Casper, WY 82602-1000; Shipping Address: 7383 6WN Road, Casper, WY 82604-1835; or call toll free: (800) 443- 9250; International, call: (307) 266-3838.

Introduction

Surveys by the National Transportation Safety Board point to some aspect of the fuel system, somewhere from the tank to its ultimate use at the engine intake valve, as a cause of a large percentage of those aircraft accidents attributed to mechanical failure. This may well be true because of the complexity of some of the systems and because of their intolerance for error or malfunction.

Fuel metering systems, whether you call them carburetors or fuel injectors, are simply mechanical devices that must measure out the proper amount of liquid fuel, determined by the amount of air the engine is taking in; atomize, then vaporize the fuel, and feed it into the cylinders. These systems are quite simple in that they obey the basic laws of physics; yet, at the same time, are quite complex because all their systems interrelate and any change in one function will be reflected into the others.

Carburetors and fuel injectors have an aura of mystery and are often blamed for performance deterioration for which they are not at fault. It is the purpose of this IAP Inc. text to familiarize the A&P with the operating principles of the systems found in float carburetors, as well as those in pressure carburetors and fuel injection systems. It is not intended to replace the manufacturer's service manuals, but rather to provide the background information that will make these vital manuals of more value.

Chapter I
Theory Of Energy Transformation

A. Source Of Energy

The internal combustion engine used in our modern aircraft is a form of heat engine. That is, it is a device which changes heat energy into mechanical energy. The heat energy used in this engine comes from our chief source of energy, the sun. Solar energy has been radiated to the earth, where it was changed into chemical energy in plant life, then into that of the animals when the vegetation was eaten. Then, during some great upheaval in the distant past, the plants and animals were buried beneath thousands of tons of earth. Through heat and pressure they became petroleum products as we know them today — fuel for our heat engines. Petroleum is an organic chemical, a compound of hydrogen and carbon, of the family known as **hydrocarbons**.

B. Release Of Energy

In order to release this heat energy from the fuel, we must cause a chemical reaction to take place. For this to occur, the hydrocarbon fuel must be brought into contact with a source of oxygen and the temperature of the fuel raised to its **kindling point**. When this happens, the oxygen will combine with the fuel and oxidation, or burning, occurs.

Each **molecule** of aviation gasoline, our most generally used fuel for piston-type aircraft engines, consists of eight atoms of carbon and eighteen atoms of hydrogen. This is written C_8H_{18}. In order to get complete release of the energy in this fuel, we must burn all of it; that is, we must unite all of it with oxygen. Oxygen in its gaseous form requires two **atoms** to make one molecule, and for complete burning we need two molecules of gasoline and twenty-five molecules of oxygen gas. Looking at this as a chemical reaction, we see the following has taken place:

$$2\ C_8H_{18} + 25\ O_2 \rightarrow 16\ CO_2 + 18\ H_2O + Heat$$

Three products were formed by the burning of aviation gasoline: 16 molecules of carbon dioxide (CO_2), 18 molecules of water (H_2O), and, along with the formation of these two new chemical compounds, the very thing we wanted: **Heat.**

C. Mixture Requirements For Efficient Transformation

The above chemical reaction equation shows us that a definite amount of oxygen is required to unite with the gasoline to produce water and carbon dioxide without any leftovers, either from the fuel or from the oxygen. The oxygen we use to combine with the fuel comes from the air.

Air is a physical mixture of several gases, principally nitrogen and oxygen. Nitrogen, however, being an inert gas, does not enter into this fuel-oxygen combination. Fifteen pounds of air is required to unite with one pound of gasoline to get complete burning of the fuel. If there is more air than required, the mixture will be lean, and oxygen will be left after the burning is completed. On the other hand, if there is more fuel than is required for the available oxygen (too rich a mixture), there will be free carbon left as a product of combustion. The mixture ratio of fifteen pounds of air to one pound of fuel is known as the **stoichemetric** mixture. Stoichemetric simply means the chemical combination which completely uses all of the products of the reaction. A 15:1 air-fuel ratio may also be expressed as a fuel-air ratio of 0.067. (This decimal comes from dividing 1 by 15.)

Combustion can occur with mixtures as rich as 8:1 (0.125) or as lean as 18:1 (0.055). The maximum amount of heat energy is released with the chemically correct mixture of 0.067. If the mixture is lean, there is less fuel and thus less heat energy. If the mixture is rich, there is not enough oxygen and some of the fuel will not be burned; thus, a smaller amount of heat energy will be released.

It would seem logical that since the most heat energy is released from the fuel with a fuel-air mixture ratio of 0.067, this ratio would produce the most power. This is actually not the case. The design of the intake system, the valve overlap, and the valve timing all work together to require a mixture slightly richer than the chemically perfect mixture to produce maximum power. Maximum power is normally considered to be obtained with a mixture of approximately 0.083 or 12:1.

Aircraft engines, because of the demand for light construction, are not designed to be operated with the mixture which produces perfect combustion and thus the maximum temperature. They must be operated at a point either side of this mixture, Figure 1-1, depending on the desired result: operation on the rich side will produce the maximum power, and operation on the lean side will produce the maximum range. Modern engines use the measurement of exhaust gas temperature to determine the proper setting of the mixture control. The mixture is leaned until the exhaust gas temperature reaches its peak on the EGT gauge, and the mixture is enriched until a specified drop in EGT is noted. Leaning the mixture slightly will also produce a temperature drop, but it is not normally recommended to lean the mixture from this temperature peak unless uniform distribution of mixture between the cylinders is assured.

D. Thermal Efficiency

Aviation gasoline has a heat energy content of nominally 20,000 Btu per pound. One Btu, or **British thermal unit**, is the amount of heat

energy required to raise the temperature of one pound of water one degree F.

Since there is a direct relationship between Btu and work, we can calculate the amount of work per unit of time, or horsepower, the fuel should produce.

One Btu produces 778 **foot-pounds** of work. We also know that one horsepower is defined as 33,000 foot-pounds of work accomplished in one minute. If an airplane engine burns 12 gallons of gasoline per hour, the power available from the fuel is 565 horsepower. We find this by the following calculation:

Fuel weighs 6 pounds per gallon.
$12 \times 6 = 72$ pounds of fuel per hour.
$72 \times 20,000 = 1,440,000$ Btu per hour.
$1,440,000 \times 778 = 1,120,000,000$ foot-pounds of work done in one hour.
$$\frac{1,120,000,000}{60} = \frac{18,666,660 \text{ foot-pounds of}}{\text{work in one minute.}}$$
$$\frac{18,666,660}{33,000} = 565 \text{ horsepower}$$

An aircraft engine burning 12 gallons of gasoline per hour will actually produce about 135 horsepower, resulting in a **thermal efficiency** of about 24%.

$$\frac{\text{Actual horsepower}}{\text{Theoretical horsepower}} = \frac{135}{565} = 24\%$$

E. Brake Specific Fuel Consumption

In rating an aircraft engine, we seldom use thermal efficiency; we use, instead, the **brake specific fuel consumption**. This is the number of pounds of fuel burned per hour for each **brake horsepower** produced. The engine we used in our example has a BSFC of 0.53 pounds of fuel, per brake horsepower, per hour. This is computed by the formula:

$$\frac{\text{Pounds of fuel burned per hour}}{\text{Brake horsepower produced}} = \frac{72}{135} = 0.53$$

F. Production Of Power

One horsepower is equal to 33,000 foot-pounds of work done in one minute. In an aircraft engine this power may be computed by the formula:

$$\text{Horsepower} = \frac{\text{PLANK}}{33,000}$$

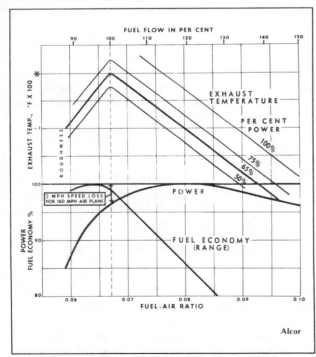

Figure 1-1. The peak exhaust gas temperature provides a reference from which the desired fuel-air mixture ratio may be determined.

P = **Brake mean effective pressure**
This is the average pressure in the cylinder during the power stroke, expressed in pounds per square inch.

L = Length of the stroke in feet

A = Area of the piston head, in square inches

N = Number of power strokes per minute. This is one half of the engine RPM

K = Number of cylinders

Pressure multiplied by area gives the number of pounds of force exerted by the expanding gases.

Force in pounds times the length of the stroke in feet gives the number of foot-pounds of work done on each power stroke.

Work per power stroke times the number of power strokes per minute gives the number of foot-pounds of work done per minute.

When this is divided by the number of foot-pounds of work per minute for one horsepower, 33,000, we have the horsepower produced by the engine.

The pilot does not have any control over the area of the piston head, the length of the stroke, or the number of cylinders. He does have control, however, of the cylinder pressure and the number of power strokes per minute by the use of the throttle and the propeller pitch control.

Two instruments allow the pilot to monitor the engine power: the tachometer and the manifold pressure gauge. The tachometer indicates the number of power strokes per minute and the manifold pressure gauge relates to the pressure within the cylinder.

Manifold pressure is measured in inches of mercury, absolute, the pressure existing in the intake manifold referenced from zero pressure. Standard sea level atmospheric pressure is 29.92 inches of mercury. The absolute pressure in the intake manifold is not the cylinder pressure, but since the manifold pressure relates to cylinder pressure, its indication is adequate for engine monitoring and control purposes. Manifold pressure may be measured at any convenient point between the throttle valve and the intake valve.

G. Factors Affecting Manifold Pressure

Manifold pressure, and thus the cylinder pressure, of an aircraft engine is affected by several factors:

1. Density Altitude

Density altitude is that altitude in standard air which compares with the existing air density. In other words, this is an easy way to indicate the relative density of the air the engine is breathing. As temperature increases, the density altitude increases, and the engine will operate as though it were at a higher altitude. As we saw previously, the combination of fuel and air takes place as a function of the weight (actually, the mass) of the air, not its volume. As the air becomes less dense (less mass per unit volume) there is a lesser amount of oxygen to unite with the fuel.

2. Humidity

Water vapor is only about 5/8 the weight of dry air, and since part of the air is displaced by water vapor, the charge in the cylinder becomes less dense; therefore, there is less mass of air to unite with the fuel. Manifold pressure is a measure of the pressure only, and does not take into consideration the density of the water vapor.

3. Carburetor Air Temperature

In the same way that water vapor decreases the density of the air without affecting its pressure, the addition of heat to the inlet air will decrease its density without changing its pressure. Heated air contains fewer molecules of oxygen for a given volume.

4. Exhaust Back Pressure

When the exhaust valve opens to scavenge the burned gases from the cylinder, some of them are unable to push their way out because of back pressure, caused by atmospheric pressure. As the airplane goes to altitude, this atmospheric pressure decreases and the diluting effect of the exhaust gases becomes less. Any exhaust gases left in the cylinder at the beginning of the intake stroke will dilute the fresh charge with air containing very little oxygen. This will decrease the amount of heat which can be released from the fuel.

5. Supercharging

Air is a physical mixture of gases in which the percentage of oxygen is essentially constant, regardless of the pressure. If the pressure of the intake gases is increased mechanically, the amount of oxygen available for combination with the fuel will be increased and so will the amount of heat energy released. Somewhere near a 5% increase in power is obtained from the ram air produced by the forward speed of the airplane. In order to get a greater power increase with sea level conditions, and to maintain sea level power at altitude, superchargers are used. A supercharger is simply an air compressor, either gear-driven from the engine, or turbine-driven by exhaust gases.

6. Compression Ratio

The more the fuel-air mixture is compressed before ignition, the higher will be the pressure and temperature after combustion occurs. Numerically, the cylinder pressure just before ignition is approximately equal to the manifold pressure multiplied by the compression ratio. For example, an engine with a compression ratio of 6:1 when operating with a manifold pressure of 26 inches of mercury (approximately 13 psi, absolute) would have an absolute cylinder pressure of 13 x 6, or about 78 psi. The final pressure after ignition is greatly affected by this initial compression pressure. The more highly the fuel-air mixture is compressed before ignition, the higher will be the ultimate cylinder pressure and temperature. The higher the temperature for a given amount of fuel and air, the lower will be the specific fuel consumption. There is a very definite practical upper limit to which we can raise the pressure and temperature in a cylinder, however. This limit is imposed by detonation.

7. Detonation

Detonation is a condition of uncontrolled burning which occurs within a cylinder when the fuel-air mixture reaches its *critical pressure and temperature*. Under normal conditions, the fuel-air mixture is compressed and ignited by the spark plugs. The mixture burns with the flame fronts progressing across the face of the piston from both sides. Ahead of the flame front, the mixture is heated and further compressed. The increase in pressure within the cylinder during normal combustion applies a push to the piston. You will notice from Figure 1-2 that the pressure rises evenly after combustion to its maximum value about twenty degrees after top dead center. If, for any reason, the fuel-air mixture reaches its critical pressure and temperature, it will explode rather than burn and will not produce an even rise in pressure and push the piston down; it will, instead, produce a sharp blow to the piston head, Figure 1-3. The pressure waves generated by the explosion travel at sonic speed and produce a ping or knock. This pinging is quite audible in automobile engines, but because of propeller noises is not generally heard in an airplane. The rapid rise in pressure and temperature imposes loads on the connecting rods, bearings, valves, and the piston head and combustion chamber walls which lead to failure.

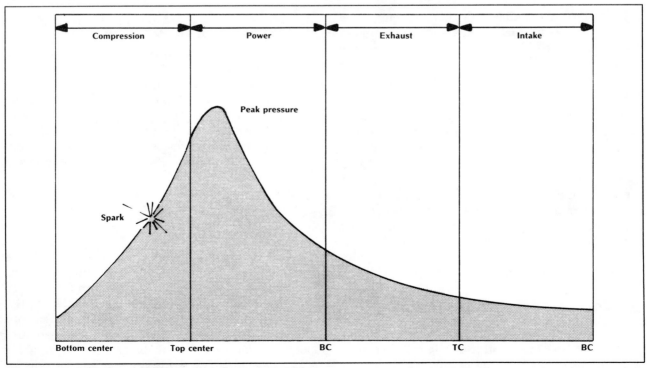

Figure 1-2. Cylinder pressure during the power stroke.

8. Pre-Ignition

There is a condition which may readily occur which will cause sure failure of an engine. The high temperatures produced by detonation will cause some sharp point such as a flake of carbon, a valve edge, or a spark plug electrode to become **incandescent**. When the piston starts up on the next compression stroke, this incandescent point will ignite the fuel-air mixture before the normal point of ignition. This condition is called **pre-ignition**. The mixture burns as the piston continues upward, and this longer burning period with its higher compression pressures will cause the mixture to detonate. The main point of pressure and temperature concentration will be the same each time, and will cause the piston or cylinder head (wherever the incandescent point is located) to erode or melt away. Holes have been melted through pistons and cylinder heads have been blown off of the barrels by detonation. Since detonation is a function of the temperature in the cylinder, effective detonation control consists of keeping the mixture temperature below its critical value.

9. Fuel-Air Mixture Ratio

The proper rate of fuel burning depends to a great extent upon the chemical composition of the gases in the cylinder. If the mixture is proper for complete combustion, the flame front will travel across the piston at a fast rate. A mixture leaner than stoichemetric will have the fuel molecules more widely scattered and the flame propagation will be slower, the mixture will still be burning when it goes out the exhaust valve, and it will cause excessive heating of the cylinder head. This can lead to pre-ignition and detonation.

10. Ignition Timing

All certificated aircraft engines in the United States are required to have dual ignition. This means that each cylinder must have two spark plugs. One reason for this is, naturally, safety in case one magneto malfunctions. Of equal importance is the fact that starting the flame front on two sides of the piston will give a more rapid burning of the fuel without the attendant high pressures that would result from the longer flame propagation if it were ignited from one side only. Some engines, because of a diluted fuel-air mixture near the exhaust valve, make use of staggered timing; that is, the spark plug nearest the exhaust valve will fire a few degrees before the other plug. This will allow the flame front to progress more evenly and meet more nearly in the center of the piston head. Operation of an engine at high-power output with a fouled spark plug, or any ignition malfunction which prevents one plug firing, can possibly cause detonation.

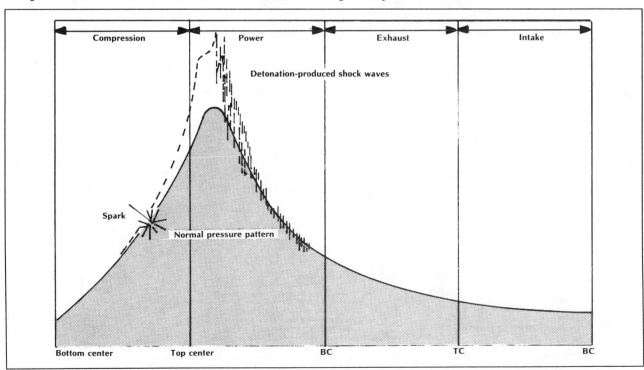

Figure 1-3. Cylinder pressure during detonation.

1. *Name two requirements for the release of energy by a hydrocarbon fuel.*

2. *Name three products formed when aviation gasoline is burned.*

3. *What is the mixture ratio range in which aviation gasoline will burn?*

4. *In what units is brake specific fuel consumption expressed?*

H. Engine Performance Charts

Before an aircraft engine is presented to the FAA for certification, the manufacturer performs a series of tests. Charts made up as a result of these tests show the relationship between manifold pressure, RPM, fuel consumption, and horsepower, both at sea level and at altitude.

1. Sea Level Performance

Figure 1-4 is typical of the performance curves furnished for a typical aircraft engine. On the left is the sea level chart. The scale across the bottom is the manifold pressure in inches of mercury, absolute, and the vertical scale shows the brake horsepower.

To use this chart, let us find the sea level horsepower at 2300 RPM and 23.75 inches of manifold pressure. First, locate 23.75 inches of manifold pressure at the bottom of the chart, and follow this up to the point it intercepts the 2300 RPM curve. Project a line horizontally to the right until it intercepts the vertical horsepower scale. For these conditions, the engine will produce 130 brake horsepower at sea level.

You will notice that the maximum pressure drops off slightly as the RPM increases. At 2400 RPM, the maximum manifold pressure is just

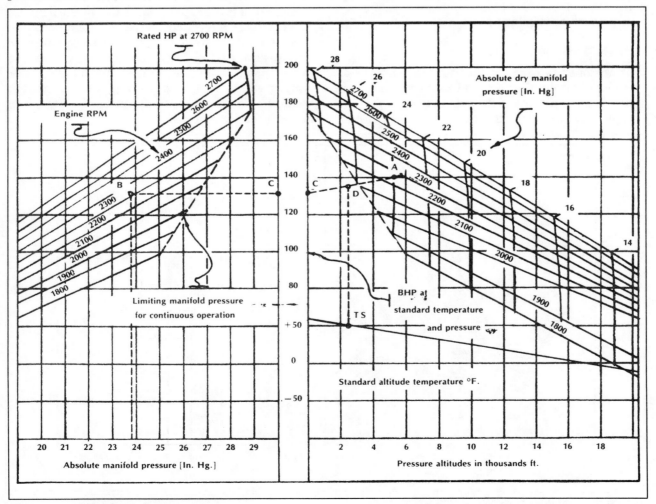

Figure 1-4. Altitude performance curve.

about 28.9 inches of mercury. At 2700 RPM, it has dropped to 28.6 inches. Friction in the induction system acting on the airflow causes this drop. As the velocity of the air flowing through the intake system increases, the maximum attainable manifold pressure becomes less.

2. Altitude Performance

As the airplane goes to altitude, the maximum available horsepower naturally decreases because there is less oxygen. If the engine were able to maintain the same RPM and manifold pressure at altitude, it would produce more horsepower. This is because there is less exhaust back pressure for the engine to work against as it expels the exhaust gases from the cylinders. The altitude performance curve of Figure 1-4 is used in conjunction with the sea level curve to indicate the maximum altitude at which we can expect to get any specific horsepower, and to give the brake horsepower produced

with any combination of RPM and manifold pressure. Instead of sea level, for example, we are at an altitude of 2500 feet. Naturally the throttle must be opened farther to get the same power. Because of the decreased density of the air at this altitude, a greater volume must flow through the carburetor to get the same number of pounds of air into the engine. Locate and mark point A on the altitude curves where the 2300 RPM line and the 23.75 inch manifold pressure arc intersect.

Carry the sea level horsepower to point C on the sea level line of the altitude performance chart. In our example, this is 130 brake horsepower.

Connect points A and C with a straight line. Locate on this line a point, D, where the 2500 foot *pressure altitude* line intersects.

Draw a horizontal line from this point D to the horsepower scale between the two charts. Here we

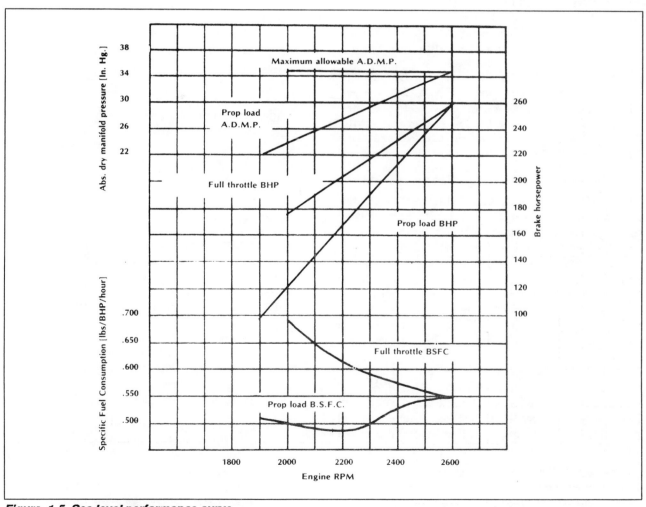

Figure 1-5. Sea level performance curve.

see that with 2300 RPM and 23.75 inches of manifold pressure at 2500 feet pressure altitude the engine will produce 133 brake horsepower.

Pressure altitude does not take into consideration variations from standard temperature which affects the density of the air. Assuming, in this hypothetical situation, we are at 2500 feet pressure altitude with an outside air temperature of +30° F. Locate, on the temperature curve at the bottom of the altitude performance chart, its intersection with the pressure altitude. In this case, it intersects at +50° F. Our temperature is +30°; therefore, the air is more dense than under standard conditions. The formula for computing the correction takes into consideration the square root of the difference in absolute temperatures; but in practice it will suffice to add one percent of the uncorrected brake horsepower for each 10 degrees the actual temperature is below standard for that altitude. If the temperature is above standard, subtract one percent for each 10° F. If the temperature scale is in Celsius, the correction factor is one percent for each six degrees above or below standard. In the example given, the temperature is 20° below standard, so we must add two percent, or approximately three horsepower, to the uncorrected 133 brake horsepower. From this, we see that at a density altitude of 1200 feet (pressure altitude 2500 feet corrected for temperature) with 2300 RPM and 23.75 inches of manifold pressure the engine will develop 136 brake horsepower.

3. Full Throttle Versus Propeller Load

Another useful set of curves, Figure 1-5, relates the manifold pressure, RPM, brake horsepower, and specific fuel consumption, in the conditions of full throttle with a dynamometer load; and partial throttle conditions with the load imposed by the propeller. Looking first at the RPM versus brake horsepower (the middle curves) we see both lines increase as RPM increases. The slope of the propeller load curve is the steeper of the two, and the two curves meet at 2600 RPM and 260 horsepower. This is the maximum power the engine can develop. Tracing back down the curve, we can find the BHP the engine will develop with any given RPM. For example, at 2200 RPM, the engine will develop 168 brake horsepower. At this RPM, the engine is capable, with full throttle, of developing 205 brake horsepower.

The manifold pressure versus RPM also uses two curves; one to show the full throttle manifold pressure, and the other the actual propeller load manifold pressure. The engine used for this set of curves is turbocharged, so the maximum allowable manifold pressure is steady for all plotted RPMs at 35 inches of mercury, absolute. In actual operation with the propeller load, the manifold pressure increases with increasing RPM until the propeller load curve meets the full throttle curve. This occurs at 2600 RPM and 35 inches of mercury.

The brake specific fuel consumption curves show the relationship between the pounds of fuel used for each brake horsepower produced, and the RPM. The full throttle curve shows, as would be expected, a relatively steady decrease in the BSFC as RPM and horsepower increase. The propeller load curve is indicative of the efficiency of the engine and shows a decrease in the BSFC up to a point. This occurs because a large increase in horsepower is obtained with a relatively small increase in actual fuel consumption. Above this point, an increase in power requires a greater effort on the part of the engine and, since its efficiency is lower, the BSFC increases. At full power, the engine has a BSFC of 0.550 and burns 23.85 gallons of gasoline per hour.

$$\frac{\text{Fuel}}{\text{consumption}} = \frac{0.550 \times 260 \text{ BPH}}{6 \text{ pounds per gallon}} = \frac{23.85 \text{ gal.}}{\text{per hour.}}$$

Under an economical cruise condition of 60% power, the engine will burn 12.5 gallons per hour. These curves are based on the use of full-rich mixtures at sea level. More economical cruise conditions are normally to be had at altitude using a lean mixture.

QUESTIONS:

5. *Refer to the performance chart of Figure 4 and answer the following questions:*
   A. *What is the sea level horsepower at 2400 RPM and 24 inches of manifold pressure?*
   B. *What is the maximum manifold pressure this engine is allowed to use for continuous operation at 2200 RPM at sea level?*
   C. *What horsepower would this engine develop at 8000 feet with 2000 RPM and 20 inches of manifold pressure if the outside air temperature is +10° F?*

6. *Refer to the power curves of Figure 5 and answer the following questions:*
   A. *What RPM and manifold pressure would be used for a 70% power cruise?*
   B. *What is the fuel consumption in gallons per hour for a 70% power cruise?*

Chapter II
Aviation Fuel

A. Requirements For Aviation Fuels

Selecting a fuel suitable for use in a particular airplane is more involved than simply deciding whether we use "regular" or "premium". The specifications for aviation fuels are laid down by the petroleum industry and are accepted by the Federal Aviation Administration. Every airplane, in its *Type Certificate Data Sheet*, has the fuel listed which is approved for it. The use of improper fuel may cause engine failure, or it can at least reduce the engine power output below that required for the airplane.

When a fuel is selected, two factors must be considered: chemical and physical. On the chemical side, the fuel must have a high heat energy content, it must be free from any constituents which form acids or gums, it must have a high boiling point and a low freezing point. It must have a low vapor pressure, and its flash point must be low enough that it can ignite readily from the spark plug, yet not so low that it is hazardous for normal handling. Physically, the fuel must be free from any contaminants, be easy to filter, and must be pumpable at very low temperatures.

B. Aviation Gasoline

The chief fuel for reciprocating engine aircraft is aviation gasoline. Aviation gasoline is a hydrocarbon fuel, refined from crude oil. The crude petroleum is distilled, and the *fractions* as they boil off are condensed into the various petroleum products. Gasoline produced in this manner is known as straight-run gasoline and constitutes the larger part of that used in airplanes. Some of the heavier fractions, unsuitable for use as aviation gasoline, are further treated by a process known as cracking. Here, the hydrocarbon is heated under pressure, sometimes with a catalyst, to break it down into products having higher volatility which are more suitable for use in gasoline.

1. Gasoline Blends

a. Paraffin Series

These are the more stable series of hydrocarbons. They are clean burning and have a high heat energy content for their unit weight, but because they are so light, their heat energy content for a unit volume is low. The paraffin series has a very low boiling point.

b. Cycloparaffin Series

Another stable series, sometimes called the napththalene series, the cycloparaffins have a lower heat energy per unit weight than the paraffins but have a higher boiling point.

c. Aromatic Series

These have a high solvency tendency and tend to dissolve or swell rubber fuel lines, rubber tanks, diaphragms, and such products. Aromatics are smoky burning and have a high density; therefore, a high heat energy per unit volume. They have a high freezing point, and the anti-detonation characteristic of this series is good.

d. Olefin Series

These are the most unstable of the hydrocarbon series used in gasolines and combine with themselves through a process known as *polymerization* to produce a gum-like residue. On their credit side, they are clean burning, have a high boiling point and a low freezing point. Because of their unstable nature, they are not found in natural petroleum products but are formed in the cracking processes.

Because no one hydrocarbon series produces all of the desirable characteristics wanted in an aviation fuel, the fuels we use are blended of certain percentages of each of the four series.

Also found in the fuel, but as undesirable constituents, are sulfur compounds which combine with other elements to produce acids which promote corrosion and damage pumps, valves, the metering system, and the engine itself.

Gums and varnishes form from the combustion of gasoline and cause rings and valves to stick and do other internal damage to the engine. Some of these gums form during storage, especially if the fuel is exposed to sunlight or to elevated temperatures. It is the high sulfur content of this type of gum that gives old gasoline its characteristic sour odor.

2. Gasoline Ratings

a. Heat Energy Content

Aviation gasoline must have a minimum of 18,700 Btu per pound. Its nominal rating is 20,000 Btu per pound.

b. Reid Vapor Pressure

Liquid gasoline does not readily combine with oxygen, so, in order to burn, it must be vaporized, or evaporated. A liquid will evaporate when the pressure of the escaping gases is greater than the pressure above the liquid, so a liquid may be caused to evaporate by either lowering the pressure above it or by raising its temperature. The amount of pressure required to hold the vapors in a liquid is known as its *vapor pressure*, expressed in pounds per square inch at a specific temperature.

Vapor pressure is measured in a Reid Vapor Pressure Bomb. Fuel is enclosed in a container, its temperature accurately controlled, and the pressure above the fuel is measured. The allowable range of Reid Vapor Pressure for aviation gasoline is from 5.5 to 7.0 psi at 100° F.

If the vapor pressure of aviation gasoline is too low, the fuel will not vaporize properly and hard starting will result, especially in cold weather. If the vapor pressure is too high, the fuel will "boil" in the lines of the fuel system. Fuel vapors released in the lines have a tendency to collect in high points and cause vapor lock, simply a bubble of fuel vapor in the line which, because of its compressibility, resists the flow of fuel from the tank to the carburetor or pump.

c. Critical Pressure and Temperature

When the fuel-air mixture in a cylinder reaches a certain pressure and temperature, it will explode rather than burn evenly. This explosion is known as detonation.

In order to get the maximum power and the lowest specific fuel consumption from an aircraft engine, the cylinder pressures must be raised as high as possible. The amount of pressure allowable is usually limited by the critical pressure of the fuel.

(1) Octane Rating

In order to rate the fuel according to its critical pressure, a comparative rating system has been established. The detonation characteristics of two hydrocarbons are used as datum values, and a variable compression ratio test engine is used to establish the detonation conditions. *Iso-octane*

(C_8H_{18}) is a member of the paraffin series of hydrocarbons and has a high critical pressure and desirable detonation characteristics. It is given a rating of one hundred. *Normal heptane* (C_7H_{16}), on the other hand, has a low critical pressure and temperature and very undesirable detonation characteristics and is given a rating of zero.

For this rating test, the fuel is run in the test engine and the compression ratio raised until a definite condition of detonation is produced. The test fuel is then switched out and a metering system put into operation in which a mixture of iso-octane and normal heptane can be fed into the engine. The ratio of octane to heptane is varied until the same detonation characteristics are obtained as were produced by the fuel under test. If the blend of standard fuels is, for example, 80 percent octane and 20 percent heptane, the fuel is given a rating of 80.

(2) Performance Number

The advent of engines with higher compression ratios has demanded fuels with antiknock characteristics even better than those of iso-octane. In order to rate these fuels, iso-octane with varying amounts of tetraethyl lead added to increase its critical pressure is used as the reference fuel. The fuel ratings with numbers higher than 100 are not octane ratings, but are *performance numbers*. *Octane ratings* and performance numbers of aviation gasolines are dual numbers, such as 80/87, 100/130, and 115/145. These dual numbers are the anti-detonation characteristics of the fuel when operating with, first, a lean fuel-air mixture ratio such as is used for cruise, and then with a rich mixture as used for take-off. For example, 100/130 performance fuel has the same anti-detonation characteristics as iso-octane when operating with a lean, cruise mixture ratio, and the same as iso-octane with a specified amount of tetraethyl lead added when operating with the rich mixture used for take-off. Because of the danger of detonation from using a fuel of lower than recommended octane or performance rating, recognition of the rating of the fuel is vital. For this reason, refineries add dyes to the fuel to identify the grade.

3. Fuel Additives

In order to get better anti-detonation characteristics from a particular aviation gasoline, tetraethyl lead is added. 80/87 aviation gasoline may have a maximum of 0.5 milliliter of *tetraethyl lead* (TEL) per U.S. gallon; 100/130 performance fuel may have as much as 4.6 milliliters per gallon.

This fuel additive aids in getting more power from the engine, but adds the problem of lead-fouled spark plugs.

In recent years, the petroleum industry has made a concerted effort to phase out the production of 80/87 aviation gasoline in favor of a low-lead 100 octane fuel. Rather than the 4.6 milliliters of tetraethyl lead per gallon allowed in regular 100/130 fuel, the low-lead gasoline has a maximum of two ml per gallon. This is sufficient for lubrication of parts requiring the lead and is therefore considered satisfactory for all engines requiring 100 octane fuel.

The greater amount of lead, however, has led to a great deal of spark plug fouling among engines designed to operate on 80. Engine manufacturers have taken a rather conservative view of the use of **low-lead 100 octane** and have warned that its continued use in engines designed for 80 octane gasoline may lead to decreased time between overhaul.

To distinguish between the normal 100/130 gasoline and the newer low-lead fuel, beginning in 1975, the low-lead 100 octane is being dyed blue. Formerly, blue aviation gasoline was 91/96; this has been phased out, and there should be no blue gasoline available except for the new low-lead variety.

The TEL has a lower volatility than gasoline, so under conditions of consistently low power output or uneven fuel-air distribution, some spark plugs may have their electrodes bridged over by a formation of conductive lead oxide, completely shorting out the plug. A scavenging agent, **ethylene dibromide**, is added to the fuel to combine with the lead oxide and form lead bromide. This is more volatile than the oxide and passes out the exhaust as a gas.

QUESTIONS:

1. *What is the maximum vapor pressure of aviation gasoline?*
2. *What is the meaning of the dual octane rating of aviation gasoline, such as 80/87?*
3. *What type of aviation fuel is colored blue?*
4. *What damage may result when 100 octane fuel is used in an engine designed to operate on 80 octane?*
5. *What is the function of the additive ethylene dibromide in aviation gasoline?*

C. Fuel Contamination

A review of aircraft accidents attributable to powerplant failure shows a large portion of them are due to fuel contamination. Strainers clogged with debris and water in the carburetor are chief offenders.

1. Types Of Contaminants
a. Solid Particles

Sand blown into the storage tanks or into the airplane tank during fueling operation, or rust from unclean storage tanks are solid particles which clog strainers and restrict the flow of fuel.

b. Surficants

These are partially soluble compounds which are by-products of the fuel processing or from fuel additives. They have the tendency to adhere to other contaminants and cause them to drop out of the fuel and settle to the bottom of the tank as sludge.

c. Water

Though always present in aviation fuel, water is now considered a major source of contamination since airplanes fly at altitudes where the temperature is low enough to cause entrained, or dissolved, water to condense out of the fuel to form free water. This freed water can freeze, and the resulting ice will clog the fuel screens.

d. Microorganisms

Grown from air-borne bacteria, these tiny organisms gather in the fuel and lie dormant until they come into contact with free water. The bacteria grow at a prodigious rate as they live in the water and feed on the hydrocarbon fuel, and on some of the **surficant** contaminants. The scum which they form holds water against the walls of the fuel tanks, causing corrosion.

2. Detection Of Contaminants

Draining a sample of fuel from the main strainers has long been considered an acceptable method of assuring that the fuel system is clean. Tests on several designs of aircraft have shown that this cursory sampling is not adequate to be sure no contamination exists.

In one test reported to the FAA, three gallons of water were added to a half-full fuel tank. After time was allowed for this water to settle, it was necessary to drain ten ounces of fuel before any water appeared. In another airplane, one gallon of water was poured into a half-full tank, and more than a quart of fuel had to be drained before water appeared at the strainer. The tank sumps had to be drained before all of the water was eliminated from the system.

One proven method of checking for contaminants is to drain about a quart of fuel into a spotlessly clean ten-quart white enamel bucket. Stir the fuel with a clean paddle and swirl it to form a vortex cone. All of the contaminants will gather at the center of this vortex and can easily be seen.

A commercial water test kit is available, consisting of a small glass bottle and a supply of capsules containing a grayish-white powder. A 100 cc sample of fuel is taken from the tank or gas truck and put in the bottle. Into this sample is emptied one of the test capsules, the lid is screwed on, and the sample shaken for about ten seconds. If the powder changes color from gray-white to a pink or purple, the fuel has a water content of more than 30 parts per million and is not considered safe for use. This test is fail-safe; that is, any error in performing the test will give an unsafe indication.

3. Protection Against Contamination

All fuel tanks are required to have the discharge of the tank protected by an 8 to 16 mesh finger screen. Downstream of this finger screen is the main strainer, usually of the fine wire mesh type, or the paper *Micronic* type. Each fuel tank is normally equipped with a quick-drain valve where a sample of fuel may be taken from each tank on the pre-flight inspection. When draining the main strainer, some fuel should flow with the tank selector set for each tank individually. Drawing fuel when the selector valve is on the "Both" position will not necessarily drain all of the water that has collected in the lines.

4. Importance Of Proper Grade Of Fuel

Aircraft engines are designed to operate with a specific grade of fuel, and will operate neither efficiently nor safely if an improper grade is supplied to the engine.

The required grade of fuel must be placarded on the filler cap of the airplane fuel tanks, and must be determined before refueling the airplane. Manufacturers have added dyes to aviation gasoline to indicate its grade. Turbine fuel is straw colored, and both Jet A and Jet B fuel have

distinctive odors which distinguish either of them from aviation gasoline.

If an improper grade of fuel has been inadvertently used, the following procedure is recommended:

a. If the engine has not been operated:
   (1) Drain all improperly filled tanks.
   (2) Flush out all lines.
   (3) Refill the tanks with the proper grade of fuel.

b. If the engine has been operated:
   (1) Perform a compression check on all cylinders.
   (2) Inspect all cylinders with a borescope, paying special attention to the combustion chambers and the domes of the pistons.
   (3) Drain the oil and inspect all oil screens.
   (4) Drain the entire fuel system, including all of the tanks and the carburetor.
   (5) Flush the entire system with the proper grade of fuel.
   (6) Fill the tanks with the proper grade of fuel.
   (7) Perform a complete engine run-up check.

D. Fuel Handling

The aviation technician is often required to fuel aircraft and to maintain the fueling equipment. Each type of bulk storage facility is protected from static electricity discharges and from contamination as much as practical. It is the responsibility of the operator of these bulk facilities to assure that the proper grade of fuel is being put into the fuel truck and that the truck is electrically grounded to the bulk facility. The fuel filters should be cleaned before pumping and all water traps must be carefully checked for any indication of water.

When an airplane is fueled from a tank truck, it is the responsibility of the driver of the truck to position it well ahead of the airplane and to be sure the brakes are set, so there will be no possibility of the truck rolling into the plane. The truck sumps must be checked and a record made of the fuel purity. There should be a fully charged fire extinguisher on the truck, ready for instant use if the need should arise, and static bonding wire should be attached between the truck and the airplane, with a ground from the truck to the earth. A ladder should be used if needed, and a wing mat put in place to prevent damage to the airplane. The fuel nozzle must be free from any loose dirt which could fall into the tank. When inserting the nozzle, take special care not to damage the light metal of which the tank is made; do not allow the end of the nozzle to strike the bottom of the tank. After the fueling is completed, the nozzle cover is replaced and the tank cap secured. The wing mat is removed, the equipment put back onto the truck, and the hose and the bonding wire removed and rolled back onto their storage reels.

E. Fire Protection

All fueling operations must be done under conditions which allow for a minimum possibility of fire. NEVER refuel an airplane in a hangar; and defueling, as well as fueling operations, should be done in the open. Electrical equipment that is not absolutely necessary for the fueling operation should not be on, and fueling should not be done in the proximity of radar operation; sufficient electrical energy can be absorbed by the airplane that a spark could jump and ignite the fuel vapors. In case a fire should occur, it can be best brought under control with a dry powder or carbon dioxide (CO_2) type extinguisher. Soda-acid or water type extinguishers are not recommended; because the fuel is lighter than water, it would float away, spreading the fire. The dry powder or CO_2 should be swept back and forth across the fire allowing the agent to settle into the fire, cutting off its supply of oxygen and extinguishing the flame.

QUESTIONS:

6. *What damage could be suspected if an engine requiring 100 octane fuel has been operated with 80 octane?*
7. *What types of fire extinguishers are best suited for gasoline fires?*

Chapter III
Basic Fuel Metering

A. Requirements For Fuel Metering

In order for an engine to develop its power most efficiently, the fuel must be mixed with exactly the correct weight of air. The proper volume of this mixture must be distributed to all cylinders uniformly, and this volume must be controllable by the pilot. The mixture ratio must be variable to provide for full power or for economy, as the operating conditions require, and compensation must be made for changes in air density caused by temperature or altitude.

Absolute dependability is an essential characteristic of aircraft fuel metering systems, and the system must operate under conditions of moisture, dust, vibration, and engine heat without any adverse reactions.

Modern aircraft engines are being operated with cylinder pressures so high that any mismanagement of the fuel air ratio can cause detonation and ruin an engine in a very few seconds. The fuel metering system must be efficient for full power operation and at the same time meter the fuel economically for extended cruise conditions.

B. Development Of Fuel Metering Systems

1. Primitive Systems

The fuel metering system of the Wright brothers' first airplane consisted of raw gasoline dripping into a hot area of the water jacket. The air for the induction system flowed through this area and picked up fuel vapors on its way into the cylinders. The Manley engine used on the Langley Aerodrome had a slightly improved method, in which fuel dripped into a metal container filled with wooden balls. Air from the induction system flowed over these balls, picked up fuel vapor, and carried it into the cylinders.

2. Interim System

In the years between the simple drip type devices and the most modern computer-type systems, the float carburetor has been the standby in the field of aircraft fuel metering. In this system, a float operated valve maintains the fuel in the carburetor at a constant level below the tip of the discharge nozzle. Air entering the engine flows through a **venturi** which produces a pressure drop and causes the fuel to be drawn out of the float bowl and mixed with the induction air.

3. Complex Systems

Pressure carburetors and fuel injection systems, which are actually computers, are now used to weigh the air entering the engine, and mix it with the proper weight of fuel to provide the desired operating fuel-air mixtures.

C. Systems Of A Typical Aircraft Float Type Carburetor

1. Main Metering System

This system provides a uniform fuel-air mixture as the airflow varies.

a. Production Of Pressure Drop

All of the air burned in an engine must pass through the carburetor and specifically through the venturi. A venturi as shown in Figure 3-1 is a specially shaped restrictor placed in the main air passage. The principle of operation of the venturi is simply one of exchange of forms of energy.

Energy exists in two forms: potential, manifest as pressure; and kinetic, manifest as velocity. According to the law of conservation of energy, we can neither create nor destroy energy, but we can alter its form. If energy is neither added nor taken away, any increase in **kinetic energy** will result in a decrease of **potential energy**. As the airflow for the engine passes through this venturi-shaped restrictor, its speed, kinetic energy, is increased, just as water increases its speed as it flows through shallow areas to form rapids. This increase in speed causes a corresponding decrease in potential energy pressure.

b. Fuel Metering Force

Liquid fuel is delivered from the tank to the carburetor through a fine mesh wire screen, Figure 3-2, and into the float bowl or float chamber, Figure 3-3. A needle valve operated by the float keeps the fuel in the bowl at a constant level. As fuel is used from the bowl, the float tends to drop, opening the valve, allowing more fuel to enter the chamber.

Located in the center of the venturi, with its end near the most narrow point, is the discharge tube, or nozzle, Figure 3-4. This nozzle is connected by the main fuel passage to the float bowl. The top of the discharge nozzle is slightly above the level of the fuel in the bowl. The difference between the height the fuel rises in the discharge nozzle with no air flow, and the edge of the nozzle is very critical, and the force required to lift the fuel this distance is known as the fuel metering force. This force is one of the critical factors in a float type carburetor.

The fuel metering force is generated by a pressure differential. The float bowl is vented to atmospheric pressure from an area behind the venturi so the existing atmospheric pressure forces the fuel out through the discharge nozzle. With no airflow, the pressure on the discharge nozzle is exactly the same as that in the float bowl, and no fuel flows. As air flows through the venturi, the pressure at the discharge nozzle drops below that in the float bowl, and fuel flows out the nozzle.

The maximum amount of fuel which can flow out of the float bowl is limited by the main metering jet, Figure 3-4.

c. Airbleed

One of the disadvantages of this type of arrangement is the uneven fuel-air mixture which results as the air flow changes. The reason for this change in mixture ratio is easy to see if we consider a simple arrangement such as shown in Figure 3-5. As the pressure drop between the discharge nozzle and the float bowl increases due to an increase in airflow, more fuel flows and the mixture becomes richer. A wide open *airbleed*, such as shown in Figure 3-6, will produce exactly the

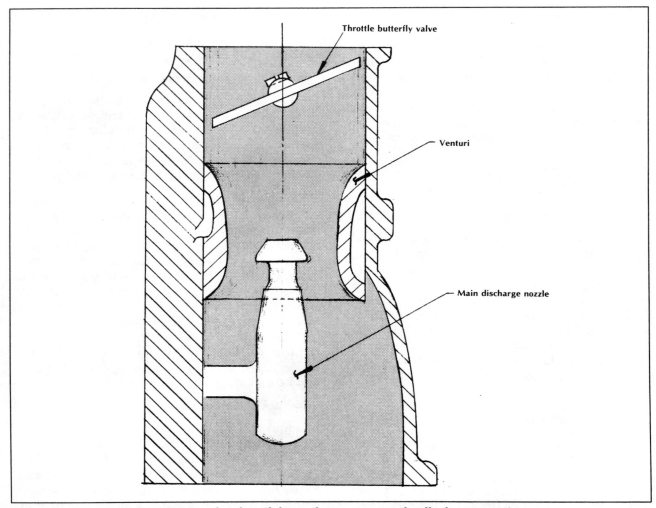

Figure 3-1. The venturi accelerates the air and drops the pressure at the discharge nozzle.

opposite results. As the airflow through the venturi increases, airflow through the airbleed increases faster than the fuel flow through the main metering jet, and the mixture grows progressively leaner. If the conditions shown in these two configurations are combined into a single operation, the leaning tendency of one will cancel the enriching tendency of the other, and the fuel-air mixture will be essentially constant as airflow changes. This is done by restricting the main airbleed as shown in Figure 3-4. The size of the airbleed is critical. Exactly enough air must be admitted to the fuel on the way to the discharge nozzle to keep the fuel-air mixture ratio constant. When the airflow through the venturi is low the pressure differential between the discharge nozzle and the float bowl is relatively small. There is a correspondingly small flow of fuel through the main metering jet and air through the

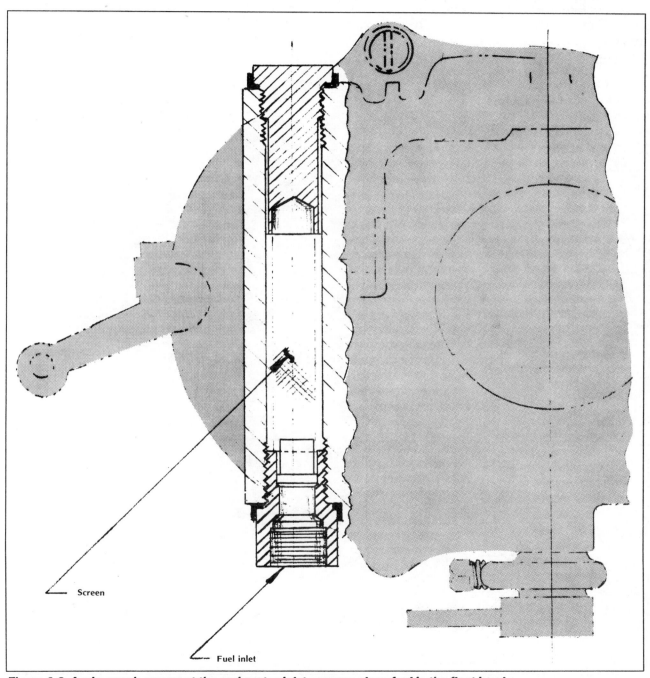

Screen

Fuel inlet

Figure 3-2. A wire mesh screen at the carburetor inlet assures clean fuel in the float bowl.

airbleed jet. As the airflow increases, the pressure drop increases, and the flow of fuel and the flow of air both increase in an essentially constant ratio.

Another function of the airbleed is to aid in the atomization of the fuel. It introduces air into the stream of fuel, breaking it up into tiny bubbles, or an emulsion of air and fuel. This emulsion is less dense than liquid fuel and may be brought up to the lip of the discharge nozzle more readily. The larger surface area of the emulsion also allows it to vaporize much more readily than if it were liquid fuel.

d. Airflow limiter

In a reciprocating aircraft engine, all of the air used to combine with fuel must pass through the venturi of the carburetor. The throttle butterfly valve, Figure 3-4, located downstream of the venturi, controls the amount of airflow into the engine, but with the throttle in the wide open position, the venturi becomes the airflow limiting device. The size of the venturi is therefore critical, and is chosen to provide the proper air velocity, and the proper pressure drop for the volume of air required by the engine.

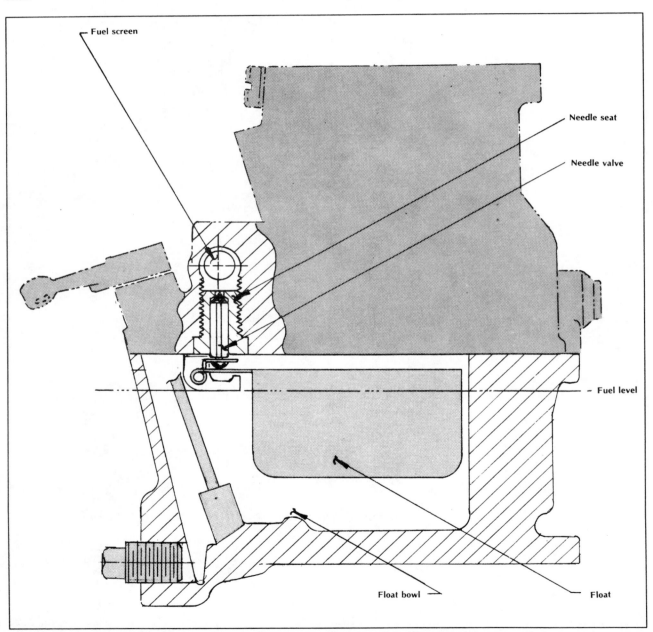

Figure 3-3. The fuel level maintained by the float and needle valve is critical for proper metering. .

The amount of air entering the engine at full throttle is a function of the pressure drop across the venturi. Any way of increasing the air pressure at the inlet, such as ram air or turbo-charging, increases the airflow into the engine, and any obstructions such as a clogged air filter will produce a corresponding power decrease of the restricted airflow.

The speed of the engine determines the pumping action of the pistons and thus the amount of air drawn through the venturi. With the same opening of the throttle butterfly valve, an increase in RPM will bring more air into the engine and more fuel from the float bowl.

QUESTIONS:

1. *What provides the low pressure at the discharge nozzle?*

2. *What limits the maximum amount of fuel which can flow from the float bowl for any given pressure differential?*
3. *Name two functions of an air-bleed.*

2. Mixture Control System

There are two ways to meter the proper amount of fuel into the airflow: Varying the pressure drop across a fixed size orifice, and varying the size of the orifice while maintaining a constant pressure differential across it. Both methods are used to control the fuel-air ratio on float type carburetor.

a. Back Suction Mixture Control

The back suction mixture control, Figure 3-7, varies the pressure in the float chamber between atmospheric and a pressure slightly below atmospheric. This pressure variation is accomplished by

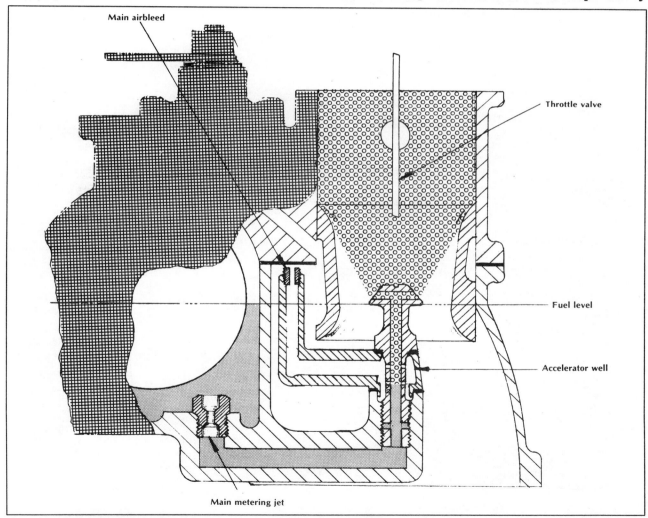

Figure 3-4. The discharge nozzle is located at the point of lowest pressure in the venturi so air pressure in the float bowl will force fuel out.

19

the use of a control valve located in the float chamber vent line. The float chamber is vented to the low pressure area near the venturi through a suction channel. This lowers the pressure in the float bowl. When the vent valve is opened, the pressure in the float bowl is raised to essentially atmospheric pressure, and a differential pressure exists across the main metering jet. This causes fuel to flow out the discharge nozzle. When the vent is closed, pressure in the float chamber decreases to a point essentially the same as the discharge nozzle. This lack of pressure differential stops the flow of fuel.

b. Variable Orifice Mixture Control

A more common way of varying the fuel-air ratio is to control the fuel flow by changing the size of the opening between the float bowl and the discharge nozzle. The float chamber has an unrestricted vent to maintain atmospheric pressure on the fuel in the float bowl. A needle valve such as is seen in Figure 3-8, or a stepcut rotary valve, Figure 3-9, is located in series with the main metering jet. When the valve shuts off the flow of fuel completely, the engine cannot run. This is the *idle cut-off* position. When the valve is opened, fuel flows to the discharge nozzle and is metered by the valve as long as the area of the opening in the valve is smaller than the area of the main metering jet. When the mixture control valve, is fully open, or in the full-rich position, the area of the opening of the mixture control is larger than the area of the main metering jet, and the jet limits the amount of fuel which can flow to the discharge nozzle.

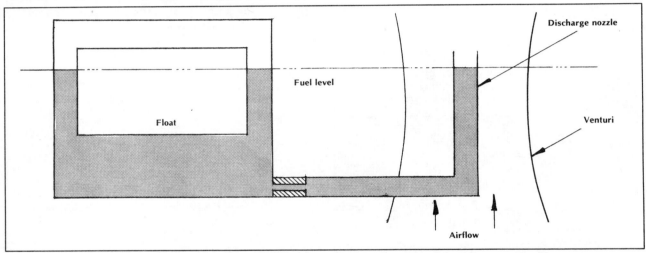

Figure 3-5. In this arrangement, the fuel-air mixture will enrich as the airflow increases.

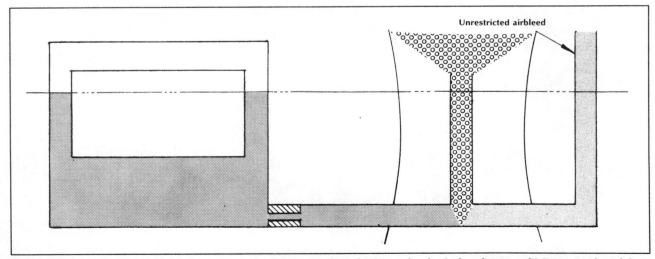

Figure 3-6. In this arrangement, air is easier to move than fuel, so the fuel-air mixture will lean as the airflow increases.

3. Idle System

At engine speeds below about 1000 RPM, the airflow through the venturi is not sufficient to produce a pressure drop at the main discharge nozzle great enough to discharge the fuel, so an auxiliary system is provided. The throttle butterfly valve restricts the air which flows into the engine, and during idling is almost closed and the only air which flows into the engine must pass around the edge of the disc. The velocity of the air at this point is naturally quite high, and the pressure at the edge of the valve is low. In the wall of the throttle body, Figure 3-10, where the butterfly valve almost touches, are two or three small holes or idle

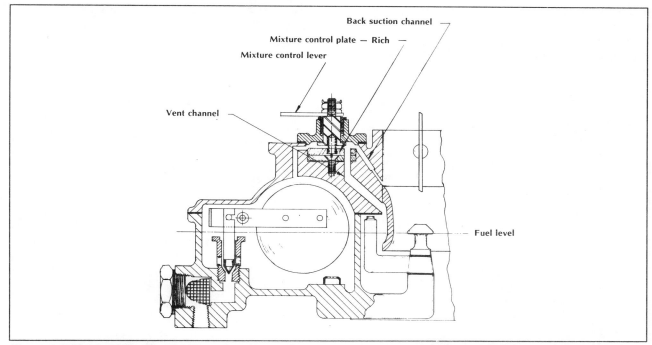

Figure 3-7. *The back-suction mixture control controls the mixture by varying the pressure drop across the metering orifice.*

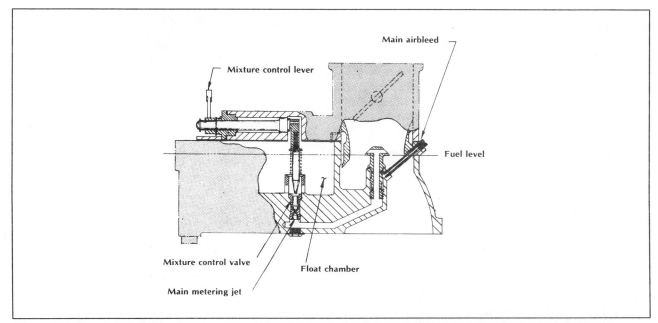

Figure 3-8. *The needle-type mixture control controls the mixture by varying the size of the metering orifice.*

21

discharge ports. These ports are connected by an idle emulsion tube to a supply of fuel between the float bowl and the discharge nozzle. This emulsion tube incorporates the idle metering jet and the idle airbleed. The upper idle discharge port is fitted with a tapered needle valve to control the amount of fuel-air emulsion allowed to flow from the discharge ports when the throttle valve is closed. The idle RPM of the engine is adjusted by varying the amount of throttle opening, by the throttle stop screw shown in Figure 3-11. The idle mixture, which determines the relative efficiency of burning, is controlled by the needle valve, Figure 3-10. When the mixture is adjusted to the most combustible ratio for all cylinders, the engine will operate most efficiently, and the manifold pressure will be its lowest. When the throttle is opened, the butterfly valve moves down, extending the area of low pressure over the **secondary** and **tertiary** idle discharge ports. This provides the fuel required for operating in conditions of off-idle, yet with not enough airflow to allow fuel to be drawn from the main discharge nozzle.

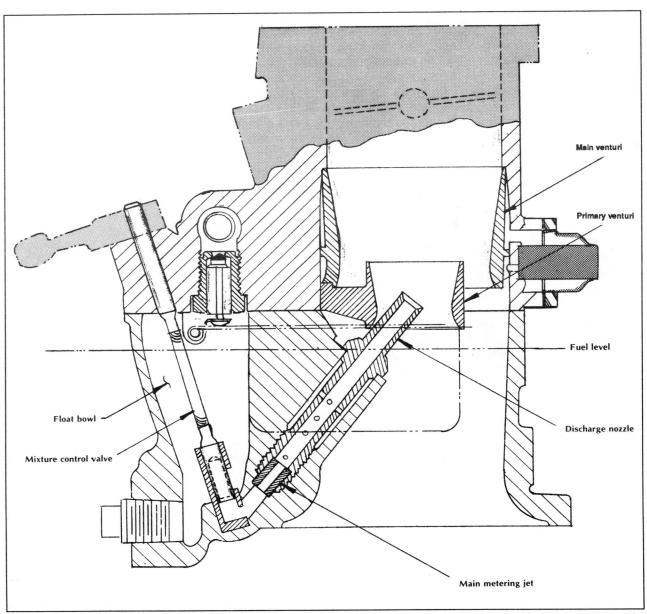

Figure 3-9. Fuel flows from the float bowl, through a step cut rotary mixture control valve, the main metering jet and on out the discharge nozzle.

When the engine is operated at cruise or higher RPM, the idle system serves as an auxiliary air-bleed, aiding the atomization of fuel at the higher flow rates.

QUESTIONS:

4. *Name two variables which affect the amount of fuel which may be metered into the airflow.*
5. *What does the back-suction mixture control vary?*
6. *What adjustment is made to change the idle RPM of an engine?*
7. *What adjustment is made to change the idle mixture ratio?*
8. *What is the function of the idle system during full power operation?*

4. Acceleration System

Between the time the idle system loses its effectiveness, and the time that there is sufficient airflow for the main metering system to operate, there is a tendency for the engine to develop a "flat spot," or a point where there is insufficient fuel for

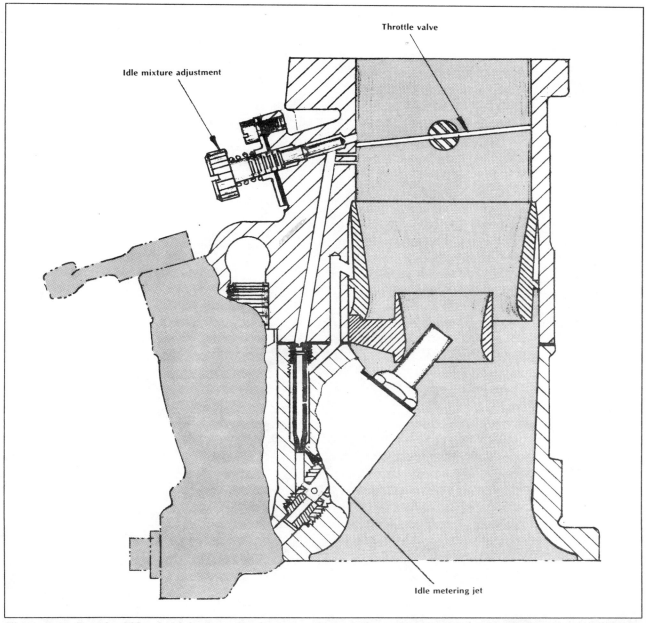

Figure 3-10. Fuel for idling is picked up after it passes through the main metering jet, brought up through the idle metering jet, mixed with air at the idle airbleed, and is discharged near the edge of the throttle valve.

continued acceleration. To overcome this condition, an acceleration system is installed.

a. Acceleration Well

The acceleration system may be as simple as the acceleration well of Figure 3-4. In this simple system, an enlarged annular chamber around the main discharge nozzle at the main airbleed junction stores a supply of fuel during idling. When the throttle is opened suddenly, this fuel is readily available between the airbleed and the discharge

nozzle to produce a rich mixture at the time the mixture would otherwise be too lean.

Engines which require more fuel for this transition use a pump.

b. Movable Cylinder Type Accelerator Pump

This type of pump, Figure 3-12, uses a brass cylinder operated by direct linkage from the throttle control. The cylinder fits somewhat loosely over a brass piston which acts as a valve and is held

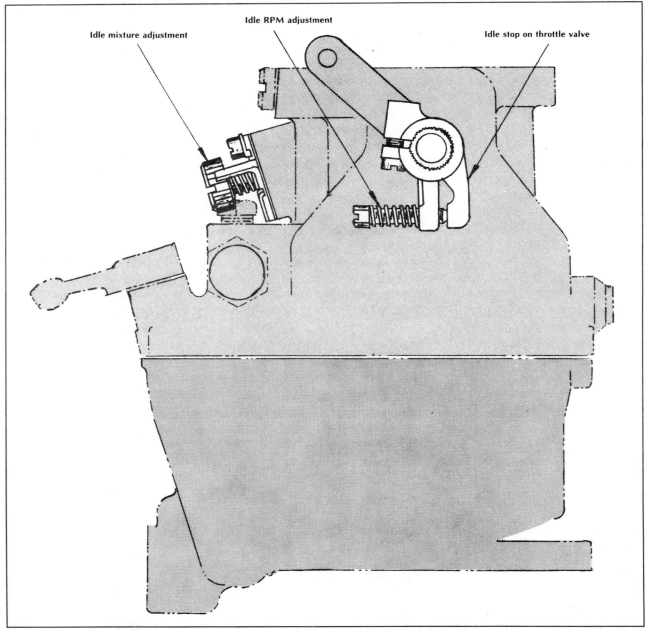

Figure 3-11. Idle mixture is adjusted by the amount of fuel allowed to flow through the idle discharge nozzle, and the idle RPM is set by the opening of the throttle air valve.

closed by a spring. When the throttle is opened suddenly, fuel is unable to escape between the piston and the cylinder wall, and the piston is forced down, opening the valve ports and forcing fuel out through the accelerator pump discharge nozzle. When the throttle is closed or moved toward the closed position, the cylinder moves up. The piston closes the valve and fuel fills the cylinder. Slow movement of the throttle allows fuel to escape around the sides of the piston rather than pushing it down.

c. Movable Piston Type Accelerator Pump

Figure 3-13 shows a leather packing type piston, held against the walls of the pump bore by a coiled spring. The pump is actuated by a linkage from the throttle. When the throttle is closed, the piston moves upward, filling the cylinder with fuel from the float bowl through a ball type check valve. When the throttle is opened, the piston moves downward, closing the ball check valve, and forcing the fuel out past the discharge check valve into the airstream through the accelerator pump discharge nozzle. The piston is mounted on a spring loaded, telescoping shaft. When the throttle is opened, fuel in unable to immediately discharge because of the restriction of the nozzle, so the shaft telescopes, compressing the spring. The spring pressure sustains the discharge, providing a rich mixture during the transition period.

5. Power Enrichment System

Aircraft engines are designed to produce maximum power consistent with their weight. They are not, however, designed to dissipate all of the heat the fuel is capable of releasing, so some provision must be made to remove some of this heat. This is done by enriching the fuel-air mixture at full throttle. The additional fuel absorbs this heat as it changes into a vapor. Power enrichment systems are often called economizer systems because they allow the engine to operate with a relatively lean, economical mixture far all conditions other than full power, Three relatively common systems are used: the needle type, airbleed type, and back suction system.

a. Needle Type Enrichment System

In Figure 3-14, an enrichment metering jet is located in parallel with the main metering jet between the float bowl and the main discharge nozzle. An enrichment or economizer valve is in series with the enrichment jet and is held on its seat by a spring. When this valve is closed, no fuel can flow through the enrichment jet and all metering is done by the main jet. The enrichment valve is opened by physical contact with the throttle linkage, as the throttle nears the full open position. When it is, open, fuel flows through both the main jet and the enrichment jet.

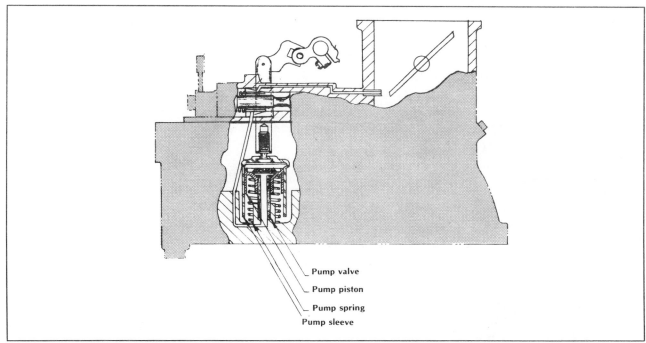

Pump valve
Pump piston
Pump spring
Pump sleeve

Figure 3-12. The movable cylinder forces fuel out the accelerator discharge nozzle when the throttle is opened suddenly.

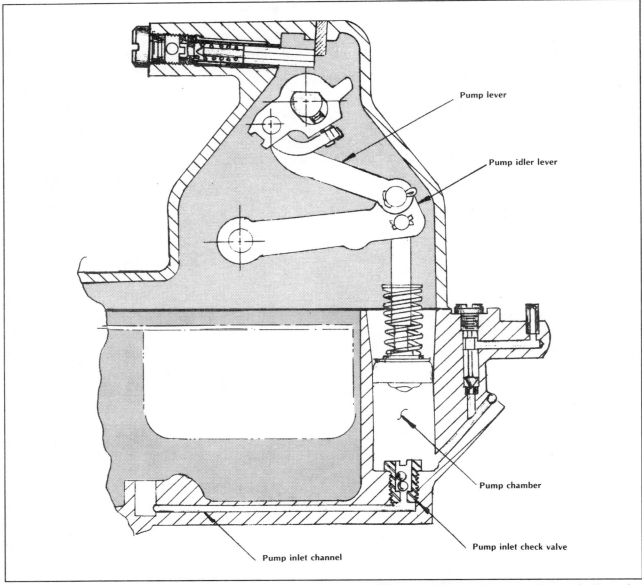

Figure 3-13. *The movable piston pump picks up fuel from the bottom of the float bowl and discharges it through a pump discharge nozzle in the venturi.*

b. Airbleed Enrichment System

As we saw earlier, an increase in air velocity through the venturi produces an increased pressure drop which enriches the mixture. To prevent this enrichment, an airbleed of a very specific size is incorporated between the float bowl and the discharge nozzle. For any given airflow through the venturi, increasing the size of the airbleed will lean the mixture and decreasing the bleed air will enrich it. In the airbleed enrichment system, the air for the airbleed comes from the float chamber, Figure 3-15, and passes through an airbleed metering valve. This valve is held open by a spring.

An arm, actuated by the throttle, closes the air metering valve, enriching the mixture when the throttle is fully open.

c. Back Suction Type Enrichment System

For all conditions other than full throttle, the float bowl is vented to a slightly low pressure, near the throttle valve, as well as ram air from behind the venturi. When the throttle is opened wide, the pressure at the port above the venturi increases, allowing the pressure in the float bowl to increase, enriching the mixture for this condition, Figure 3-16.

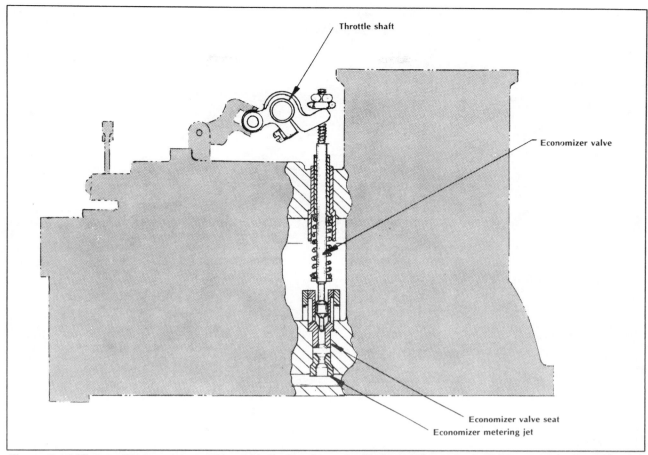

Figure 3-14. *The needle-type economizer adds fuel to the main discharge through an enrichment jet in parallel with the main metering jet.*

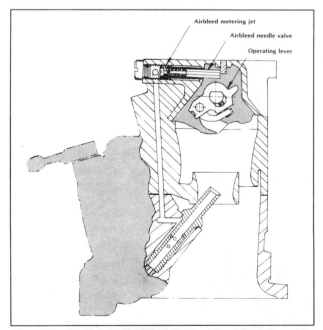

Figure 3-15. *The airbleed enrichment system restricts the main airbleed for full throttle enrichment.*

QUESTIONS:

9. What is the purpose of the acceleration system on an aircraft carburetor?
10 Why is a power enrichment system also called an economizer system?
11. Is the fuel-air mixture enriched or leaned when the main airbleed is restricted?

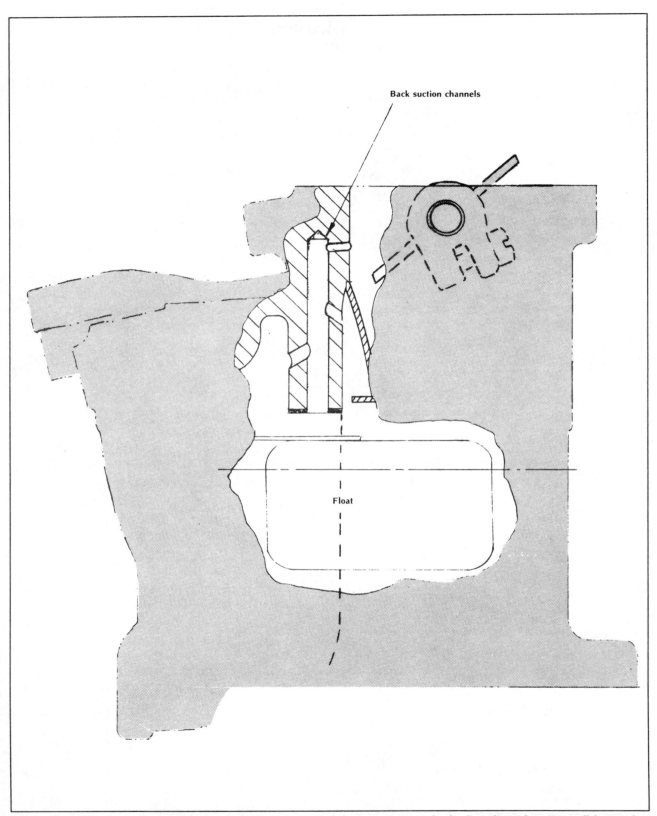

Back suction channels

Float

Figure 3-16. The back-suction economizer holds a very slight low pressure in the float bowl for all conditions other than full throttle operation.

Chapter IV
Float Carburetor Service And Maintenance

Most float carburetors used on certificated aircraft in the United States at this time are manufactured by the Precision Airmotive Corporation. This includes Marvel Schebler designs formerly manufactured by Facet/Marvel Schebler as well as Stromberg Bendix carburetors manufactured under license for Bendix Corporation.

Precision Airmotive Corporation manufactured units have the five basic systems previously discussed, even though they differ in the mechanical details of the systems.

Servicing carburetors must be done according to the recommendations of the manufacturer and both of these manufacturers have available for the aircraft technician a full set of service manuals and parts lists. The carburetor, as with any other appliance, must be maintained in the configuration and with the parts lists by which they were certificated.

The use of parts other than those specifically approved by the manufacturer will render the carburetor technically un-airworthy and will compromise its functions.

A. Inspection

1. Preflight

At each preflight inspection, the pilot should determine that there is no fuel leaking from the carburetor. Leaking fuel is evidenced by fuel dye stains on the carburetor body or in the cowling below the carburetor.

2. One Hundred Hour Inspection

A more comprehensive inspection of the entire fuel system is performed on the one hundred hour or annual inspection. The carburetor gets special attention as the fuel bowl is drained of any sediment, and the fuel strainer removed and cleaned. The air filter is cleaned or replaced. Paper type filters are usually replaced, whereas the cloth covered wire screen types are washed in solvent and blown out with compressed air.

All of the controls are checked to be sure there is no indication of binding or looseness. Particular attention is paid to the throttle shaft and its connections. Looseness of the throttle shaft in its bushings allows an air leak which destroys the calibration of the carburetor.

B. Overhaul

There is usually no particular number of operational hours between overhauls specified by the manufacturer. Good operating practice, however, dictates that at the time of engine overhaul, the carburetor, also, should be completely overhauled. Operating beyond this time can cause poor fuel metering which could lead to detonation and subsequent damage to freshly overhauled engines.

1. Disassembly

Disassemble the carburetor in a clean work area where all of the parts may be laid out systematically. All of the work must be done according to the manufacturer's overhaul manual.

2. Cleaning

After the carburetor has been disassembled and a preliminary inspection made of all the parts for wear or breakage, the entire unit is cleaned. First, wash all of the parts in a solvent such as *varsol* or *Stoddard solvent*. This will remove the grease and dirt. Dry the parts with compressed air, and immerse them in a decarbonizing solution. Carburetor decarbonizer is normally of the water-seal or glycerine-seal type, in which water or glycerine floats on the top of the active ingredients to prevent evaporation of the highly volatile solvents. When placing the part in the decarbonizer, it must be completely covered by the active agents, below the seal layer. A word of caution should be noted regarding some of the commercially available decarbonizers. Some are more active than others and will attack certain metals used in carburetors. Be sure to check the instructions before using them and use extreme care that the decarbonizer does not get on your skin or in your eyes. Should this happen, wash the affected areas with running water. In case you get it in your eyes, see a doctor immediately. After the parts have been in the decarbonizer for the appropriate time, remove them, rinse them in hot water, and dry them thoroughly with compressed air.

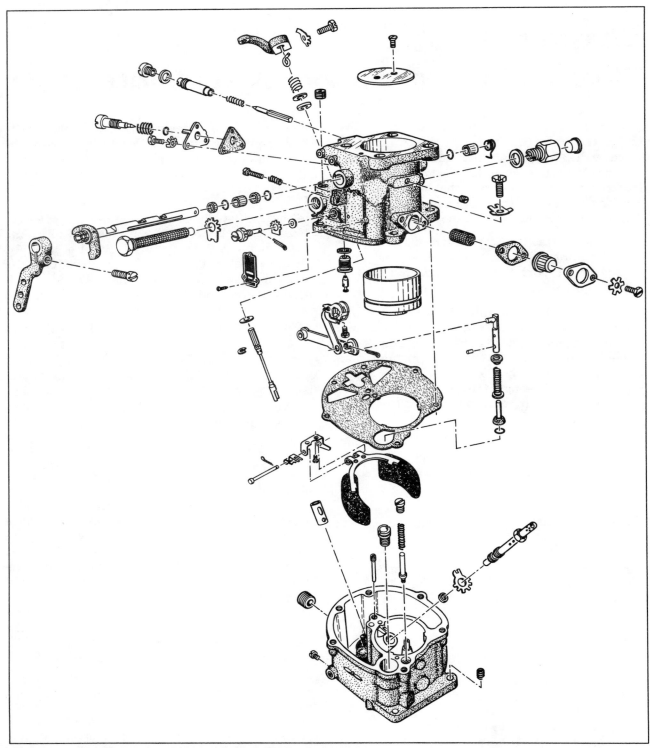

Figure 4-1. Exploded view of typical aircraft float carburetor.

3. Inspection

After all of the parts have been cleaned, they must be carefully inspected for any indication of damage or wear. Needle valves and seats should be especially examined for indications of grooves or scratches. Some models of Bendix carburetors allow the needle valve and seat to be lapped together to facilitate complete sealing, but all

Precision Airmotive carburetors require the float valve and seat assembly to be replaced with new units at each overhaul. All of the parts subject to wear should be checked against a table of limits or replaced, again following the instructions of the manufacturer in detail.

4. Parts Replacement

The throttle shaft bushings are subject to the most wear, and will likely have to be replaced. Precision Airmotive recommends about a 0.003 inch loose fit for the throttle shaft in the bushing. The old bushings are driven out by screwing a bushing removal tool into the bushing and driving it out with a hammer. When the new bushings are to be inserted, the holes should be cleaned out and the new bushings pressed in, using an arbor press and the proper size tool. The bushings are line reamed to assure that they are in perfect alignment. When reaming a bushing, be sure the reamer is turned in the cutting direction, both as it goes into the bushing and as it is drawn out. Reversing the direction of the reamer dulls the cutting edge and causes scratches on the inside of the bushing. Precision Airmotive now uses an oilite bronze bushing instead of stainless steel. When these bushings are used, the outside surface is lightly coated with Locktite compound and inserted into the bushing hole. An aligning tool is inserted through both bushings and the Locktite allowed to cure for two to four hours at room temperature. The dimensions of the hole for this type of bushing are not nearly so critical as when pressing a bushing in to be reamed. Locktite can fill clearances up to about 0.005 inch.

Throttle shaft packings between the throttle bore and the float bowl in the MSA carburetors must be replaced. Leaking packings cause considerable trouble and an easy method to check before proceeding is recommended. Invert the casting and pour a test liquid into the cavity to cover packings. Blow compressed air from the outside. If leaking is observed, replace the packings and retainers. A LEAKING OR WORN INNER PACKING CREATES A LEAN CONDITION. A LEAKING OUTER PACKING CAUSES A RICH CONDITION.

5. Reassembly

In reassembly, many operations require the use of special tools. It is poor economy to use anything other than the proper tool for some of these specialized jobs since an incorrect tool may damage a part costing far more than the tool.

Most carburetor bodies are made of aluminum alloy castings. When installing straight plugs or jets, apply a small amount of engine oil to the threads. When installing tapered plugs, insert the plug into the casting for one thread and apply a small amount of thread lubricant such as "Titeseal" to the second thread of the plug. Screwing the plug into the hole squeezes the lubricant between the threads and prevents galling. Extreme care should be taken to see that none of this compound is allowed to get inside the carburetor since it is insoluble in gasoline and may plug jets or passages.

The needle seat and valve are installed with the float, and the float level is one of the more critical adjustments of this type carburetor.

MSA carburetors have the float suspended from the throttle body and the proper float level is measured by slipping the shank of the proper size twist drill between the gasket and the float with the throttle body inverted; Figure 4-2. The drill should touch the float but not cause it to rise. If the float level is not correct, it may be adjusted by adding or removing shims from below the valve seat. Adding shim thickness increases the float clearance and lowers the fuel level in the float bowl. Removing shims has the opposite effect. After getting the proper float level, the side clearance of the float in the bowl is checked, Figure 4-3.

A special tool consisting of a cut-away float bowl is installed over the float, and a drill rod gauge passed completely around the float. The float should not be so close to the body that the gauge will bind at any point around either of the two floats. This clearance may be adjusted by loosening and repositioning the float bracket.

The amount of float drop should be checked by turning the throttle body right side up, Figure 4-4, and measuring the clearance between the gasket and the tip of the float.

Adjustment of this distance is made by grinding or filing the float bracket tang.

Floats mounted in the fuel bowl are adjusted to provide the proper level of the fuel in the bowl. The bowl assembly with the needle, seat, and float installed is mounted on the test bench and leveled both parallel and perpendicular to the float axis. Fuel of the proper specific gravity with the correct inlet pressure is fed into the bowl. The distance between the parting surface of the bowl and the level of the fuel is measured with a depth gauge. A

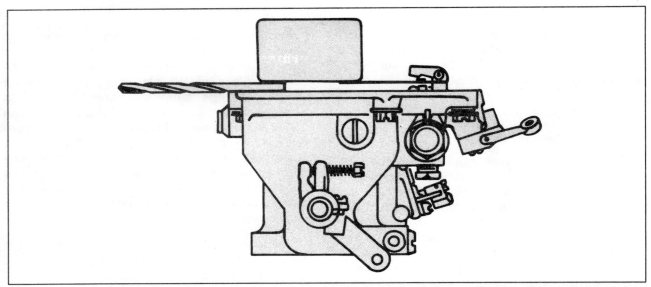

*Figure 4-2. The proper float level is measured with the appropriate twist drill **between the tip of the float and the gasket.***

correction for specific gravity other than standard is made according to the following table:

TEST FUEL SPECIFIC GRAVITY	CORRECT FLOAT LEVEL
0.675	Subtract $1/16$" from Specified Level
0.685	Subtract $3/64$" from Specified Level
0.693	Subtract $1/32$" from Specified Level
0.700	Subtract $1/64$" from Specified Level
0.710	Use Specified Level
0.720	Add $1/64$" to Specified Level
0.727	Add $1/32$" to Specified Level
0.735	Add $3/64$" to Specified Level
0.745	Add $1/16$" to Specified Level

If the fuel level is too high, shims may be added beneath the needle seat. A low fuel level is raised by decreasing the shim thickness. When measuring the fuel level, be sure the scale is held away from the wall of the bowl. The fuel has a tendency to "wet" the bowl wall, and the level at the wall will be higher than the correct measurement taken in the open part of the bowl.

Apply the test pressure specified by the manufacturer to see that the needle valve does not leak. Precision Airmotive recommends six pounds of fuel pressure be applied to the fuel intake for fifteen minutes. The fuel should not rise to the lip of the discharge nozzle in this time. This may be checked by looking into the discharge nozzle with an otoscope.

After the carburetor has been assembled, the economizer or enrichment system should be adjusted. The needle type used on the Bendix carburetors is adjusted by setting the throttle butterfly valve at the angle specified in the overhaul manual, and adjusting the lower nut on the economizer needle until it just contacts the forks. Lock the adjustment by screwing the upper nut tight against the lower.

The airbleed type economizer used by Precision Airmotive on MA4-5,-6 series, is adjusted by opening the throttle wide and adjusting the depth to which the air metering valve is screwed into the

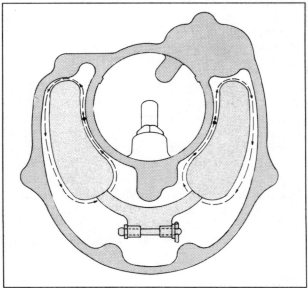

Figure 4-3. A gauge made from a float bowl with the bottom cut out is placed over the floats and the proper size twist drill must pass completely around both floats without binding.

throttle body This may be checked by either a depth gauge or a special air metering pin gauge, Figure 4-5.

C. Installation

1. Mounting

After the carburetor has been overhauled, or has been received from an accessory shop to be installed on an engine, it is checked to be sure the proper safeties and seals are intact. The serial number is recorded in the engine records, and you must assure yourself that the parts list number or assembly number for the carburetor is that required for your particular engine. Mount the carburetor on the engine using a new gasket and torque

the hold-down nuts as specified by the engine manufacturer.

Connect all of the controls and make sure the cockpit control moves through its complete travel and the stop on the carburetor is reached before the stop in the cockpit. In the case of multi-engine aircraft, the controls for all engines must be aligned in both the full forward and the full rearward position. The carburetor air scoop should be installed with particular attention paid to the fully open and fully closed position of the air valve. The air filter should be checked to see that there is no leak around the filter element where unfiltered air could be drawn into the carburetor. Before connecting the fuel line, it is a good practice to open the fuel valve and drain a small amount of fuel out

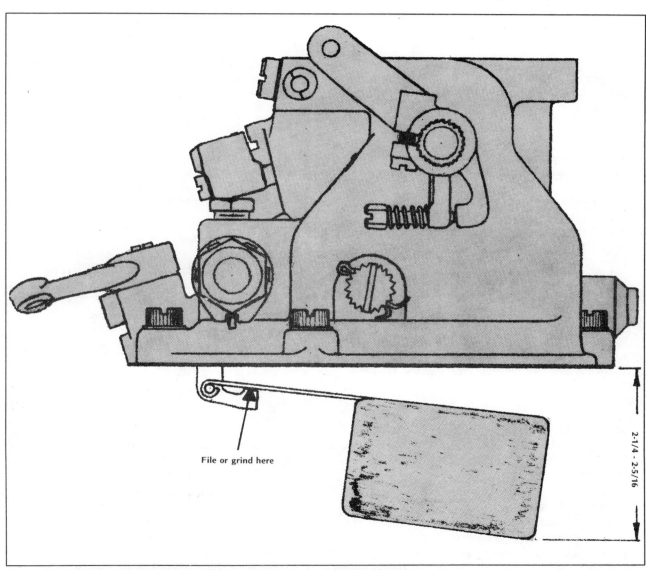

File or grind here

2-1/4 - 2-5/16

Figure 4-4. If the float drop is not correct, file the tang of the float bracket.

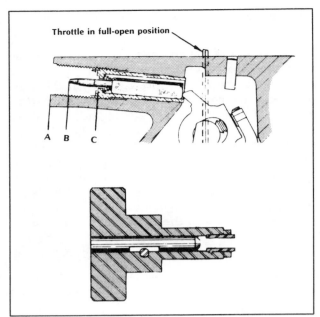

Figure 4-4. Either measure the distances A-B and A-C with a depth gauge, or, using the special tool, screw the valve body in until the pin is flush with the body of the tool.

through the line to get rid of any foreign matter which might have accumulated while the carburetor was removed. This will also assure you there is adequate flow of fuel to the carburetor.

2. Adjustment

After a repaired or overhauled carburetor is mounted on the engine, the engine must be run and the idling RPM and manifold pressure adjustments made. Before attempting to adjust anything on a carburetor, make certain that the other systems of the engine are functioning properly. After the proper warm-up, run the engine up to full power and check for the proper static RPM and manifold pressure. Check the magnetos to be sure both ignition systems are functioning properly with the magneto drops well within the allowable limits.

After you know that the engine is functioning properly, pull the throttle back and hold the RPM at the desired speed with the throttle. With the RPM held constant, adjust the idle mixture until the engine runs smoothest. If the engine is equipped with a manifold pressure gauge, the operator in the cockpit should signal when the manifold pressure is at its lowest value. This indicates the mixture is properly set. After making this adjustment, the engine should be run up to near full throttle to clear the spark plugs of any fouling

which might have occurred during this prolonged idling. Return the throttle to the desired RPM and adjust the idle speed screw until it just contacts the throttle stop. Increase the RPM and bring the throttle back against its stop to make sure there is no slippage in the linkage, and that the engine idles at the same RPM each time the throttle is retarded.

A final check of the correctness of the idle adjustment is made by pulling the mixture control back to the cut-off position with the engine idling. The RPM should rise somewhere between 10 and 35 RPM, depending on the engine, before it stops running. This slight rise before a complete drop-off indicates the idle mixture is properly set. A clean drop-off without any rise indicates the mixture is too lean. If the rise is above that specified by the engine manufacturer, the mixture is too rich.

After all of the proper checks indicate that the carburetor and the engine are functioning properly, a final inspection must be made of the installation. Check for indications of fuel leaks, loose rigging, missing safeties, or any incomplete work. Signing off the work in the engine records completes the installation procedure.

D. Servicing

1. Troubleshooting

For some reason, the carburetor seems to be a mysterious component and comes away with more than its share of the blame for performance deterioration. Fortunately, though, careful troubleshooting will eliminate the carburetor as the offender more often than not. Carburetors seldom change their calibration or operating characteristics without some outside influence, and these changes usually build up over such a time period that a warning is given.

Before assuming a carburetor to be at fault when troubleshooting an engine problem, isolate the carburetor.

a. Be sure both ignition systems check out and have the proper RPM drop when checking each system separately.
b. Be sure the engine develops the proper RPM and manifold pressure when making a full throttle static run-up.
c. Be sure that all the cylinders have the proper compression.
d. Be sure the carburetor air filter is clean and the proper filter element is installed.

e. Be sure the proper fuel pressure is supplied to the carburetor.
f. Be sure the fuel filter is clean.
g. Be sure the proper propeller is installed.
h. If the propeller is constant speed, be sure the governor is properly adjusted.
i. Be sure the muffler is not causing an excessive back pressure on the exhaust system.
j. If the performance deterioration has been noticed as a drop in RPM, be sure the tachometer is accurate.

After all other possibilities have been eliminated and the fault persists, the carburetor may be legitimately suspected. If it is at all possible, before opening it up, exchange the suspected carburetor with a similar one known to be good, and then run the engine. If the trouble is still present, the carburetor is not at fault; but if the trouble no longer exists, the carburetor has pretty well proven itself to be the culprit.

Float carburetor servicing logically divides itself into three levels, and the level attempted by an A&P technician should be governed by his experience and the availability of parts and equipment.

2. Level I

The first level of service may be considered all that can be done with the carburetor on the airplane. It consists of checking the control linkages for proper travel, freedom of movement, and proper contact with the stops. The fuel lines and air hoses are checked for kinks, distortions, or indication of leakage. The main fuel filter and carburetor strainer are checked on this level of service to assure the proper amount of fuel is being delivered to the carburetor. The air filter may be checked for the proper installation and to be sure that no air leaks into the system around the filter. The carburetor heat valve should be checked for proper travel and for any leakage of warm air into the carburetor when the control is in the "cold" position.

The idle RPM and mixture can be adjusted to provide the smoothest running engine at the closed throttle speed recommended by the airplane manufacturer.

While this level of service requires a knowledge of engine and carburetor operation and the same professional integrity as any other aircraft maintenance, it can be performed with the very minimum of stock and equipment. Replacement air filters and fuel filter gaskets are all that is required; no special tools are needed for this level of service.

3. Level II

Maintenance facilities which perform work beyond that normally considered as line maintenance do what might be considered a second level of service. This requires that the carburetor be removed from the airplane and opened for closer inspection and replacement of parts. This level of maintenance should never be attempted without the proper replacement parts available.

Level II consists essentially of removing the carburetor from the engine and thoroughly cleaning and inspecting its exterior. If the carburetor has been flooding, the needle and seat may be replaced with the new parts having the proper part numbers, and the float level adjusted. All interior passages should be inspected with an otoscope while the carburetor is open, and any obstructions blown out with compressed air. The carburetor is reassembled, using new gaskets, safety wired, and reinstalled on the engine where it is given the normal run-up tests, final adjustment, and safeties.

4. Level III

Level III is major overhaul. The carburetor is completely disassembled, and all parts cleaned with the recommended carburetor cleaner, rinsed, and dried with compressed air. All passages are carefully inspected with an otoscope, and the carburetor reassembled, with installation of all the new parts recommended by the manufacturer and furnished in the overhaul kit. The manufacturer's recommendations must be followed to the smallest detail, and no alterations made with hopes of "improving" on the manufacturer's engineering and experience.

QUESTIONS:
1. *How often should float carburetors be overhauled?*
2. *What is meant by a water-seal decarbonizer?*
3. *How much thread lubricant should be used when installing a tapered pipe thread plug in a carburetor fuel bowl?*
4. *What type of instrument may be used to inspect the drilled passages in a carburetor for cleanliness?*
5. *When adjusting the idling on an engine using a float carburetor, do you try to get the highest or lowest manifold pressure for the desire RPM?*
6. *When adjusting the rigging of a carburetor control should the control hit the stop in the cockpit or on the carburetor first?*

Chapter V
Pressure Carburetors

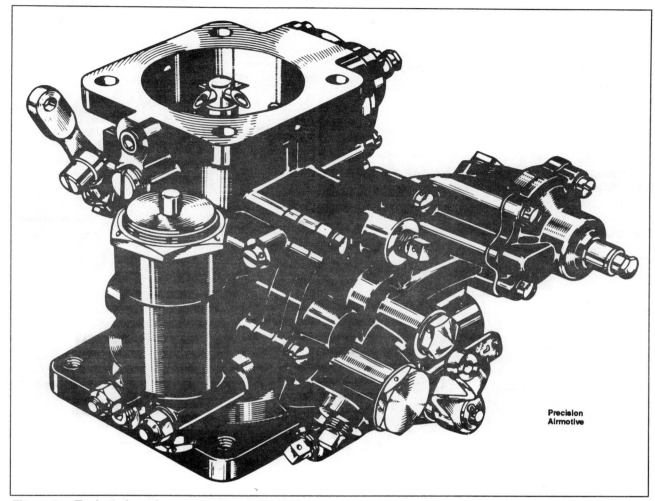

Precision
Airmotive

Figure 5-1. Typical single barrel pressure carburetor.

A. Characteristics Of Pressure Carburetors

Recognizing the limitations of the more simple float carburetor, steps have been taken to overcome them with the pressure carburetor. These limitations are essentially:

Susceptibility to icing

Uneven fuel-air mixture distribution.

Critical with respect to attitude.

Metering a function of air volume, not mass.

The pressure carburetor utilizes a closed fuel system, one in which the fuel is not open to the atmosphere at any point from the tank to the discharge nozzle, as it is in the bowl of the float carburetor. Fuel leaves the tank under pressure from the boost or auxiliary pump, goes through the filter and the engine pump to the carburetor. Here fuel is metered and directed to the discharge nozzle.

Pressure of the fuel delivered to the metering jet is controlled by the volume and density of air flowing into the engine. In this way, the fuel flow becomes a function of the mass air flow.

The Bendix PS5C, Figure 5-2, and PS7BD, Figure 5-3, are typical of the modern pressure carburetors used on light reciprocating engine aircraft, and are the units discussed here.

1. Air Metering Force

Air flows into the engine, passing first through the inlet air filter and into the carburetor throttle body, Figure 5-3; and then through the venturi, past the throttle valve and discharge nozzle into the intake manifold. As the air enters the carburetor body, some of it flows into the channel around the venturi where its pressure increases due to its decrease in velocity. This impact pressure is directed into chamber A of the computer or regulator unit. Any change in the pressure of air entering the carburetor changes the pressure in chamber A.

Air flowing through the venturi produces a low pressure proportional to the velocity of air entering the induction system. This low pressure is directed into chamber B of the regulator where it operates on the opposite side of the diaphragm from the impact air pressure. These two air forces work together to move the air diaphragm proportional to the volume of air entering the engine.

The *mass* or weight of air is a function of the air *density* and to modify the effect of air volume to reflect its density, an *automatic mixture control* is placed in the vent line between the two air chambers. When air density decreases, the automatic mixture control opens the vent, decreases the pressure drop across the diaphragm, and lowers the metering force.

2. Fuel Metering Force

Fuel enters the carburetor from the engine pump under a pressure of approximately 9 to 14 pounds per square inch, and passes through a fine mesh wire screen in chamber E on its way to the poppet valve.

The amount the poppet valve opens is determined by a balance between the air metering force

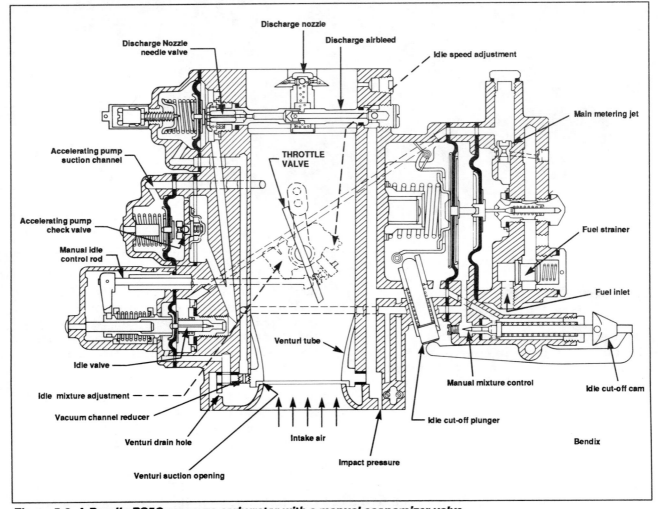

Figure 5-2. A Bendix PS5C pressure carburetor with a manual economizer valve.

and the regulated fuel pressure. The air metering force moves the diaphragm to the right, opening the poppet valve.

When the poppet valve opens, the fuel flows from chamber E into D and exerts a force on the fuel diaphragm, moving it back enough to allow the spring to close the poppet valve. The fuel pressure in chamber D is, in this way, regulated to be proportional to the mass of air flowing into the engine.

When the engine is idling with not enough airflow to produce a steady air metering force, the large coil spring in chamber A forces the diaphragm over and opens the poppet valve to provide the fuel pressure required for idling.

Fuel from chamber D, regulated but unmetered, flows through the main metering jet and through the idle needle valve. For all conditions other than idle, this valve is off its seat enough that its opening is larger than the main metering jet, so no metering is done by the idle valve. Fuel flows to the discharge valve, and the discharge nozzle. Air from the impact annulus is mixed with the fuel in the nozzle to produce a spray for better vaporization.

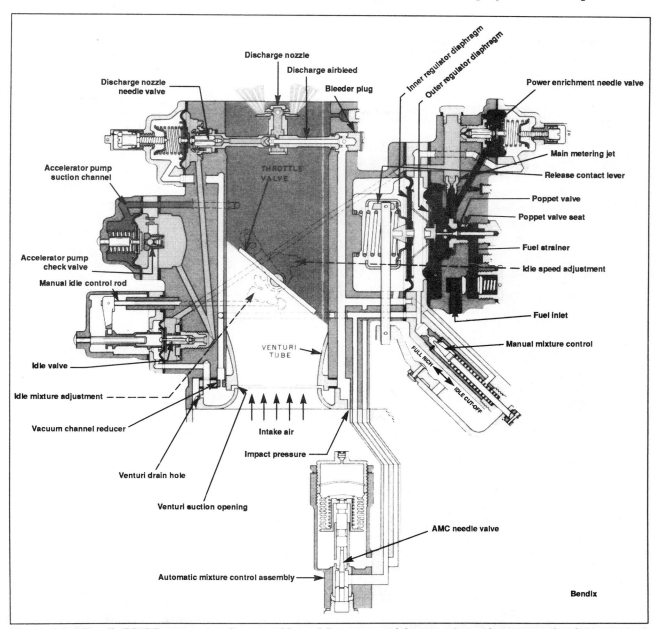

Figure 5-3. A Bendix PS7BD pressure carburetor with an airflow-type enrichment valve and an automatic mixture control.

The spring loaded diaphragm type discharge valve provides a fast and efficient cut-off when the mixture control is placed in the Idle Cut-off position. When the fuel pressure drops low enough, a spring forces the needle valve onto its seat, stopping all flow of fuel from the nozzle. This valve also provides a constant pressure downstream of the metering jet; so the variable pressure from the regulator will force a flow through the jet proportional to the mass air flow.

3. Mixture Control System

As altitude increases, the air density becomes less, and unless a correction is made for this, the mixture will enrich and the engine lose power. To maintain an essentially constant fuel-air mixture, the pilot must decrease the weight of the fuel flowing to the discharge nozzle. This is done by decreasing the pressure differential across the air metering diaphragm by opening the bleed between the two air chambers.

When the pilot wishes to stop the engine, he pulls the mixture control to the Idle Cut-off position. The mixture control needle valve is pulled back so the pressures in chambers A and B are essentially equalized. When the control is in this position the idle spring is depressed and its force is removed from the diaphragm, closing the poppet valve and shutting off all of the fuel to the metering sections.

An automatic mixture control relieves the pilot of the necessity of regulating the mixture as altitude changes. A brass bellows filled with helium and attached to a reverse tapered needle varies the flow of air between chambers A and B as the air density changes. An inert oil in the bellows damps out vibrations. This automatic mixture control, by varying the amount of airbleed between the two chambers, maintains a pressure differential across the air diaphragm appropriate for any air density.

4. Idle System

The idle system of the Bendix PS carburetor controls both the idle air and the idle fuel. All of the air which flows into the engine during idle must flow around the almost closed throttle valve. The amount this valve is held away from closing is controlled by the idle speed adjustment, an adjustable stop on the throttle shaft extension. The amount of fuel allowed to flow during idling is regulated by the amount the idle fuel valve is held off its seat by the control rod, as it contacts a yoke on the throttle shaft extension; Figure 5-4.

5. Acceleration System

A single diaphragm pump is used on most carburetors of this type to provide a momentarily rich mixture at the main discharge nozzle when the throttle is suddenly opened.

The accelerating pump is located between the idle valve and the discharge nozzle, with one side of the diaphragm vented to the manifold pressure, downstream of the throttle. The other side of the diaphragm is in the fuel line, between the main metering jet and the discharge nozzle. The coil spring in the air side compresses when the manifold pressure is low and fuel fills the pump. When the throttle is opened, the manifold pressure increases; the spring pushes the diaphragm over and forces the fuel out the discharge nozzle, momentarily enriching the mixture.

Some pumps used with this series of carburetors have a divider in the fuel chamber with a combination check and relief valve and a bleed. The valve allows a rapid discharge of fuel when the throttle is first opened, but soon seats, and a lesser, but sustained flow of fuel discharges through the pump bleed. When the throttle is suddenly closed, the decrease in manifold pressure causes a rapid movement of the pump diaphragm, and the check valve closes to prevent the pump starving the discharge nozzle. This would cause the mixture to go momentarily lean.

6. Power Enrichment System

Two types of systems are used in Bendix PS carburetors to enrich the mixture under conditions of full throttle; one system operates as a

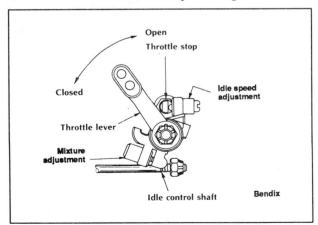

Figure 5-4. The idle RPM is adjusted by the amount the throttle valve is allowed to close, and the idle mixture by the effective length of the idle control shaft.

function of the airflow, and the other operates mechanically from the throttle valve.

a. Manually Controlled Power Enrichment Valve

A double step idle valve is used on carburetors employing this system, Figure 5-5. For operation up to approximately 65% power, the needle in the orifice limits the flow of fuel. At powers above 65%, the pressure differential across the diaphragm is great enough to pull the needle completely out of the orifice, and the fuel flow is limited by the main metering jet.

b. Airflow Power Enrichment Valve

A spring loaded valve is located in the fuel passage parallel with the main metering jet, Figure 5-3. When this valve is closed, the main metering jet limits the flow, providing a lean mixture for cruise. At the higher power settings, the venturi air pressure and unmetered fuel pressure are great enough to overcome the spring force and open the valve, enriching the mixture.

QUESTIONS:

31. What is meant by a closed fuel system?
32. What two air pressures make up the air metering force on the Bendix PS carburetor?
33. What does the manual mixture control on this carburetor regulate to control the mixture ratio?
34. What two forces are used to open the enrichment valve in the airflow type system?

B. Pressure Carburetor Installation, Service And Maintenance

A pressure carburetor is a precision piece of equipment requiring the use of a flow bench for any major maintenance or calibration. The manufacturer has established a network of authorized service facilities equipped to handle any maintenance with a minimum of down time for the airplane. Installation, inspection, and troubleshooting are, however, a routine part of the work of the aviation maintenance technician.

1. Installation

A pressure carburetor in storage is filled with preservation oil and must be conditioned or "soaked" before the fuel diaphragms have the exact pliability with which they were calibrated.

Remove the shipping plugs and drain all of the preservative oil from the regulator unit. Install the carburetor, using a new gasket, and attach the fuel line as soon as practical. Turn the fuel supply on and place the mixture control in the Rich position. Remove the pipe plug from the bottom of the regulator unit, and turn the boost pump on until clear, oil-free fuel flows out of the regulator and the

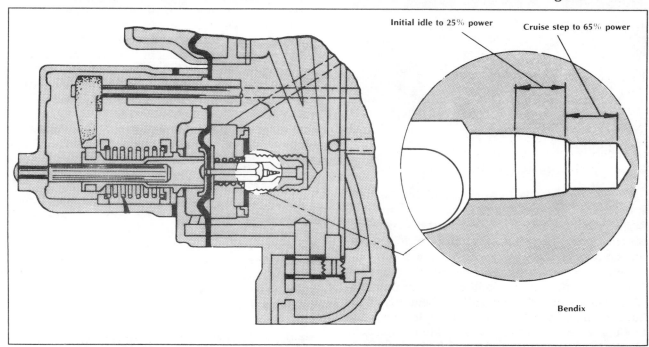

Figure 5-5. When the throttle is closed, metering is done by the shoulder of the valve; from idle, through about 25% power by the restriction caused by the needle in the orifice; and beyond 65% by the main metering set.

discharge nozzle. Place the mixture control in the Idle Cut-off position and turn the boost pump off. Allow the carburetor to stand with the fuel in it for as long a period as practical. Eight hours is recommended to completely condition the fuel diaphragms to their calibrated condition. Connect the fuel pressure gauge line and the vapor vent return line, the throttle and mixture control linkages. When screwing any tapered fittings into the carburetor be very careful that only a small amount of thread sealing compound is used, and this placed on the second thread from the end of the male fitting only. The threads, both on the fitting and in the housing, must be perfectly clean and free from burrs; apply the thread lubricant and tighten the fitting only enough to assure a leakproof seal as excessive tightening may crack the housing.

The throttle and mixture control must operate freely throughout their entire range of travel, and the stops on the carburetor should be reached before the stop on the cockpit control. The spring-back in the control system is your assurance that the carburetor control is fully actuated. Install the air filter and check the alternate air mechanism to determine that in both the direct and alternate position the valve allows an unrestricted flow of air.

2. Operation

Start the engine and allow it to warm up until the oil temperature is in the proper operating range. Check the magnetos to be sure both ignition systems are operating properly and the engine develops full power. The engine fuel pump pressure must be within plus or minus one pound of the inlet pressure recommended for the particular carburetor. If an adjustable pitch propeller is used, place the control in low pitch and turn the electric boost pump on.

3. Idle Adjustment

Adjust the throttle to approximately 600 RPM and slowly pull the mixture control to the Idle Cut-off position. Watch the tachometer as you lean the mixture. The engine should pick up approximately ten RPM before it begins to cut out. Be sure to return the mixture control to the **Full Rich** position before the engine cuts out completely. A rise of more than ten RPM indicates that the idle mixture is too rich, and an immediate decrease in RPM without the momentary rise is indicative of too lean an idling mixture. If the engine is equipped with a manifold pressure gauge, its indication may be used in place of the tachometer.

The correct mixture is indicated if the manifold pressure holds steady as the mixture control is moved toward Idle Cut-off, then rises as the RPM decreases. If the pressure drops, then rises, the idle mixture is too rich. If it increases immediately, the mixture is too lean.

Adjust the idle mixture by moving the idle adjustment screw one or two notches in or out as needed, and repeat the check procedure until you have the proper indication. When adjusting the idling, clear the engine by momentarily opening the throttle to approximately 2,000 RPM each time a change is made in the setting. After making the proper mixture adjustment, set the idle RPM and adjust the throttle stop. Check to see that the engine returns to the same RPM each time the throttle is pulled back.

4. Enrichment Valve Adjustment

Carburetors with the manual enrichment system, Figure 5-5, must have the enrichment valve setting checked after the idle adjustments are made. This valve has a cruise step on the idle valve and any repositioning for idling may affect the position from which the enrichment system operates. Put the proper adjusting gauge directly over the throttle stop, Figure 5-6, and open the throttle until the lever contacts the gauge. Hold the throttle in this position and adjust the enrichment valve adjusting screw until it just contacts the control rod. Tighten the locknut and safety. If the carburetor is equipped with an airflow type enrichment system, the opening of the enrichment valve is accomplished by the airflow through the carburetor. This adjustment must be made on a flow bench; it is not a field adjustment.

5. Metered Fuel Pressure Adjustment

The basis of metering of the Bendix pressure carburetor is a varying pressure differential across the fixed metering jet. This differential is achieved by holding the pressure of the discharge fuel constant with a constant pressure discharge valve. A small amount of adjustment in the field is permissible on certain models of this carburetor by adjusting the tension on the discharge valve spring, Figures 5-2 and 5-3. This adjustment may be made only on those carburetors having discharge nozzle adjustment limiters. Carburetors without this limiter could be adjusted lean enough to damage the engine.

If the engine operates rough in the RPM range between idle and cruise, it is possible that the discharge pressure could need adjusting. Before making this adjustment, it is especially important that the engine be checked for proper operation of all systems which could affect its operation. Engine oil temperature and cylinder head temperature should be in the proper operating range, and the idle RPM and mixture adjustments must be correct and both ignition systems operating properly.

Set the engine speed between 1200 and 1500 RPM, pull the mixture control back, and note the amount of rise before the RPM starts to drop off. The mixture control must be returned to Full Rich before the engine stops.

If the RPM rises, the discharge nozzle setting is on the rich side of best-power mixture. If there is no rise, the setting is at or leaner than the best-power mixture. The *off-idle mixture* may be enriched by screwing the discharge nozzle adjustment counter-clockwise, or it may be leaned by screwing it clock-wise. Make this adjustment by turning the nozzle adjustment one notch at a time until the desired performance is reached.

After making the off-idle check, the engine must be cleared and the idling checked and readjusted as necessary. Any adjustment of the idle mixture will necessitate readjustment of the manual enrichment valve.

QUESTIONS:

1. *Why should pressure carburetors be "soaked" when they are installed?*
2. *What is the final check for proper mixture ratio when adjusting the idling on an engine equipped with a pressure carburetor?*
3. *What may be adjusted to eliminate rough operation in the RPM range between idle and cruise?*

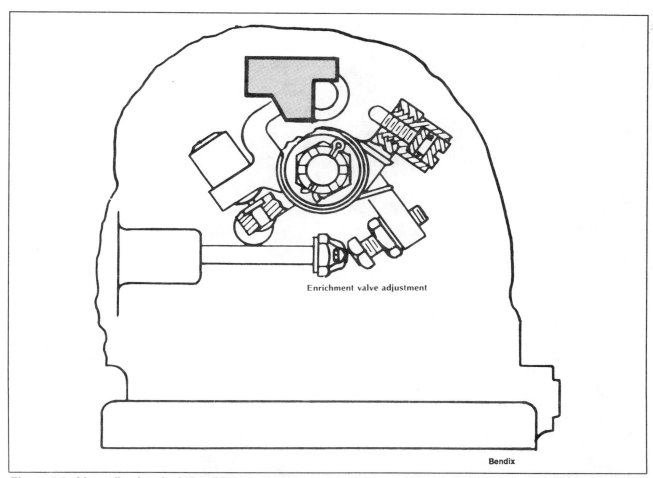

Enrichment valve adjustment

Bendix

Figure 5-6. After adjusting the idling RPM and the mixture, the manual enrichment valve must be adjusted by holding the throttle a specific distance from the stop with a special gauge and adjusting the enrichment valve adjustment screw.

Chapter VI
Precision Airmotive Fuel Injection Systems

Uneven fuel-air mixture distribution, a problem with conventional carburetors, has become of increasing importance as the horsepower requirements of modern aircraft engines continue to go up. The present day aircraft engine operates with such high cylinder pressures that an inadvertently lean mixture on an individual cylinder can cause detonation and consequent engine damage.

Some of the larger engines have, in the past, used a direct injection system with a master control unit. This was similar to a large pressure carburetor metering the proper amount of fuel into two multi-cylinder piston pumps which force the fuel directly into the combustion chambers as timed, high-pressure spurts.

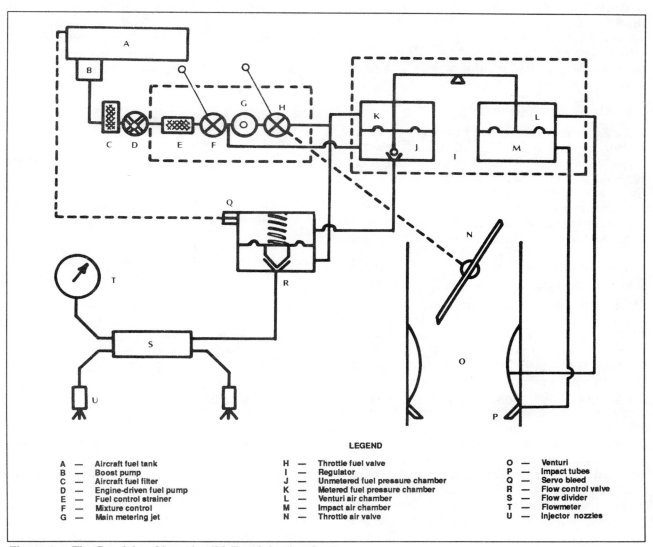

LEGEND

A	—	Aircraft fuel tank	H	—	Throttle fuel valve	O	—	Venturi
B	—	Boost pump	I	—	Regulator	P	—	Impact tubes
C	—	Aircraft fuel filter	J	—	Unmetered fuel pressure chamber	Q	—	Servo bleed
D	—	Engine-driven fuel pump	K	—	Metered fuel pressure chamber	R	—	Flow control valve
E	—	Fuel control strainer	L	—	Venturi air chamber	S	—	Flow divider
F	—	Mixture control	M	—	Impact air chamber	T	—	Flowmeter
G	—	Main metering jet	N	—	Throttle air valve	U	—	Injector nozzles

Figure 6-1. The Precision Airmotive RS Fuel Injection System.

Timed injection systems, because of their complexity, have been superseded by the more simple, yet effective, continuous flow systems.

A. Precision Airmotive RS Injection System

The Precision Airmotive RS (Reciprocating engine-Servo control) fuel injection system is a continuous flow system which meters fuel by a pressure drop proportional to the airflow across the metering orifice.

The variable pressure drop generated by the Bendix PS carburetor depends on a constant pressure discharge valve holding the pressure constant downstream of the metering orifice. In the RS system, the pressure upstream of the metering orifice is held more or less constant by the engine driven pump, and the downstream pressure is varied by a flow control valve proportional to the airflow. Refer to the line drawing of Figure 6-1 to trace the flow of fuel from the aircraft tank to the discharge nozzles.

1. Air Metering Force

Air flows through the throttle body as in any carburetor. A venturi, O, and impact tubes, P, sense the air velocity and pressure. Impact air is directed into chamber M on one side of the air diaphragm, and air from the throat of the venturi into chamber L on the other side. Any change in engine speed moves the diaphragm an amount proportional to the change in airflow.

2. Servo Fuel-Flow

Fuel comes from the tank through the fuel filter, C, and engine driven pump, D, into the fuel control, E. Here it is further filtered and a portion of the unmetered fuel, under full pump pressure, is fed to one side of the fuel diaphragm in chamber J. A ball type valve in this chamber controls the flow of fuel to the flow divider, R. The air forces tend to close the valve as the airflow into the engine increases, and the fuel metering force, the difference between unmetered and metered fuel pressure, tends to open the valve. This balance of forces meters servo fuel to the flow control valve proportional to the airflow into the engine and is relatively unaffected by any normal variations in engine pump pressure. *Servo fuel* flows through the upper chamber of the flow control valve, back to the tank, but the flow is restricted by the servo bleed, Q. When the servo flow decreases because of an increase in airflow into the engine, the pressure against the servo bleed decreases, and this allows the metered fuel to open the flow control valve. This decreases the pressure downstream of the fuel control and allows more fuel to flow into the engine. When the throttle is closed and the airflow decreases, the servo valve opens, increasing the servo fuel in the flow control valve. The pressure builds up against the servo bleed and restricts the flow of fuel to the engine.

3. Metered Fuel-Flow

Fuel passes through the strainer, E, in the fuel control, through the mixture control, F, to the main metering jet, G. When the mixture control is in the Full Rich position, the orifice is uncovered, and the fuel flows unrestricted to the metering jet. As the mixture is moved toward the lean position, the orifice becomes smaller in area than the main jet and metering is done by the mixture control. Fuel flows through the jet, and the throttle valve H, another flat plate valve similar to the mixture control, then to the flow control valve below the diaphragm, on the flow divider, S, and the nozzles, U.

4. Idle System

When the airflow is insufficient to provide an accurate placement of the servo valve in its seat, a constant head spring in the regulator positions the valve. Figure 6-2 shows the diaphragm held in the neutral position by the combined forces of the constant effort and constant head springs.

As the airflow increases, the diaphragm moves over, telescoping the shaft and compressing the constant head spring. As the diaphragm moves out of the neutral position it is aided by the constant effort spring; by the time the air metering force is sufficient for consistent metering, the constant effort spring is completely relaxed and the diaphragm position is determined by the two air pressures. Adjustment of the constant head and constant effort springs is made on a flow bench and not in the field.

The idle speed and mixture adjustments are made by the A&P technician and are similar to that of any carburetor. The engine is started, warmed up, and checked to make sure all systems are operating properly. The throttle stop is backed out so it will not limit the movement of the control in the cockpit and the RPM is held constant by the cockpit control. Adjust the idle mixture by changing the length of the rod between the throttle air valve and the throttle fuel valve, Figure 6-3.

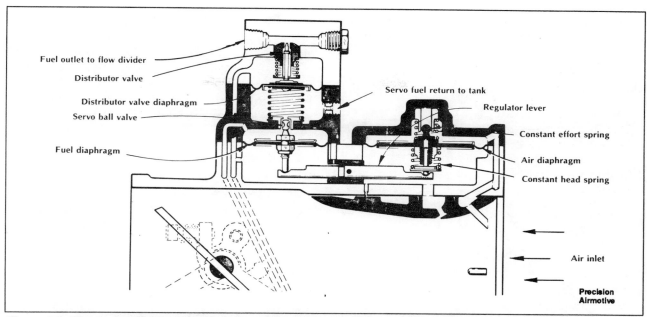

Figure 6-2. The constant head and constant effort springs in the Precision Airmotive RS injection system control idle fuel pressure until the air metering force becomes sufficient.

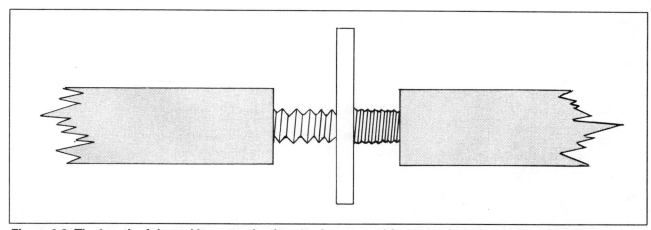

Figure 6-3. The length of the rod between the throttle air valve and fuel valve is varied to adjust the idling fuel-air mixture.

One end has coarse threads and the other fine. Turn the adjustment in the direction to screw the coarse threads into the link to shorten the rod and lean the idle mixture. Screw the coarser threads out to lengthen the rod and enrich the mixture. Adjust the idle mixture to get the lowest manifold pressure for the desired RPM, then hold the engine at the desired RPM with the cockpit control while you adjust the throttle stop screw until it just contacts the stop. As a final check, clear the engine by running it up to about 2000 RPM for a few seconds, close the throttle, and pull the mixture control slowly back until the engine begins to die. There should be approximately a 10 to 25

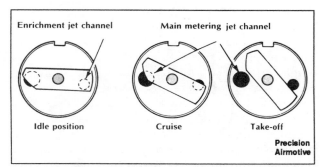

Figure 6-4. The enrichment jet, in parallel with the main metering jet, is uncovered when the throttle nears its wide open position.

RPM rise before it quits. If the RPM drops without this rise, the mixture is too lean, and if the rise is appreciably higher, the mixture is too rich.

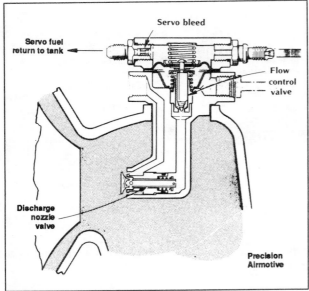

Figure 6-5. Some supercharged engines have a single-point fuel discharge into the supercharger impeller.

5. Power Enrichment System

Some models of the RS injection system enrich the mixture at full throttle by uncovering a passageway parallel with the main metering jet. The exit to this passage is covered by the throttle valve plate until the throttle is almost full open; then the passage is uncovered and the mixture enriched; Figure 6-4.

6. Flow Control Valve

The flow control valve, sometimes called the distributor valve, Figure 6-5, maintains a variable pressure downstream of the metering orifice by a balance of forces between servo pressure and metered fuel pressure. An increased airflow through the engine decreases the servo fuel pressure and allows more fuel flow, while a decreased airflow has the opposite results.

7. Flow Divider

Some models of this system use a flow divider, Figure 6-6, to which the nozzle lines to the individual cylinders attach and is the point at which the pressure measurement used as a flow indication is taken.

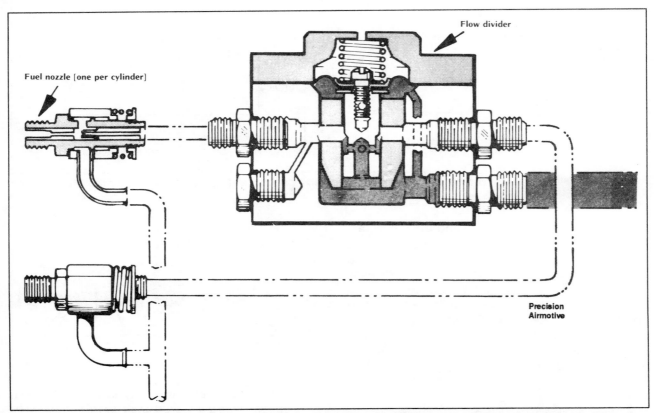

Figure 6-6. The flow divider distributes fuel evenly between the cylinders and shuts off the fuel to the nozzles when the metered fuel pressure drops below about two psi.

When the engine is idling, the nozzles do not produce enough back pressure for efficient metering and the spring loaded valve provides a steady pressure downstream of the flow control valve. Under normal flow conditions, the metered fuel pressure under the diaphragm lifts the valve out of its seat and allows unrestricted flow to the nozzles.

When the metered fuel pressure drops below two pounds per square inch, the spring closes the valve

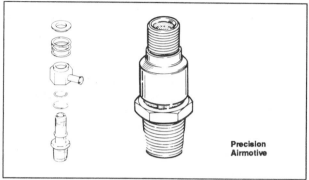

Figure 6-7. Turbocharged engines have their nozzle shrouds pressurized with turbocharger discharge air pressure. Normally aspirated engines have a screen and protective cover around their outside.

and provides a positive shut-off of fuel to the nozzles.

8. Injector Nozzles

Individual cylinder injector nozzles used with this system are of the airbleed type, Figure 6-7. Each nozzle has a calibrated orifice, a fuel chamber, an airbleed, a tight fitting screen and a protective metal shroud. Fuel flows into the nozzle and collects in the chamber until the intake valve opens and creates a low pressure in the intake chamber. The fuel and air emulsion is drawn into the cylinder where vaporization takes place immediately.

Manifold pressure on turbocharged engines is higher than outside air pressure and fuel would be blown out of the airbleed holes if other provisions were not made. In these engines, special shrouds are used around the nozzles. Turbocharger air is fed into the shroud and mixes with the fuel through the airbleed hole.

Engines having internal superchargers may have the fuel injected into the eye of the blower with a special single point injector nozzle, Figure 6-5, instead of nozzles in each cylinder.

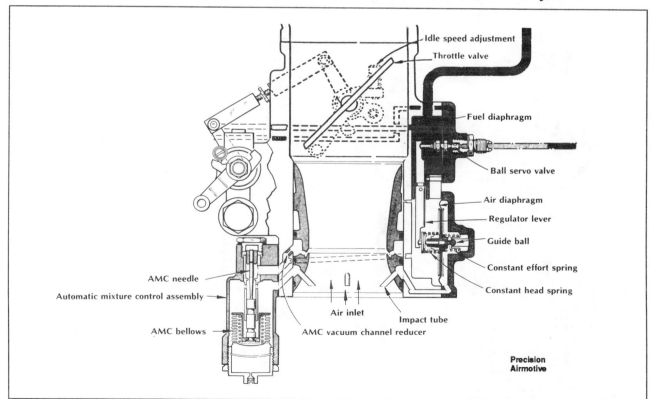

Figure 6-8. The automatic mixture control utilized an evacuated bellows-driven, reverse tapered needle valve to maintain the pressure differential across the air diaphragm proportional to the existing air density.

49

9. Automatic Mixture Control

A sealed bellows containing low pressure helium and a small amount of an inert oil senses variations in air density and moves a reverse tapered needle to control airflow through an orifice between the two air chambers. As the density of the air decreases, the bellows expands, enlarges the orifice, and decreases the pressure differential across the air diaphragm. This leans the mixture.

10. Fuel Flowmeter

The fuel flow indication the pilot has on his instrument panel is actually a pressure measurement taken across the fixed injector nozzles. The pressure drop across these fixed orifices is dependent upon the flow rate through them.

Turbocharged engines use a differential pressure gauge to measure the difference in pressure between the discharge fuel pressure and the turbocharger air pressure in the nozzle shroud.

One problem with this type of fuel flow indication should be considered when troubleshooting a fuel injection system. If a nozzle plugs up, the flow through it will be less than required but the pressure across the nozzle will be greater, so the flow meter will give an indication of **more** flow than normal.

QUESTIONS:

1. *Does servo fuel flow increase or decrease as flow through the engine increases?*
2. *What are the four pressures which make up the metering force of an RS injection system?*
3. *What is the purpose of the constant head spring?*
4. *What is the purpose of the constant effort spring?*

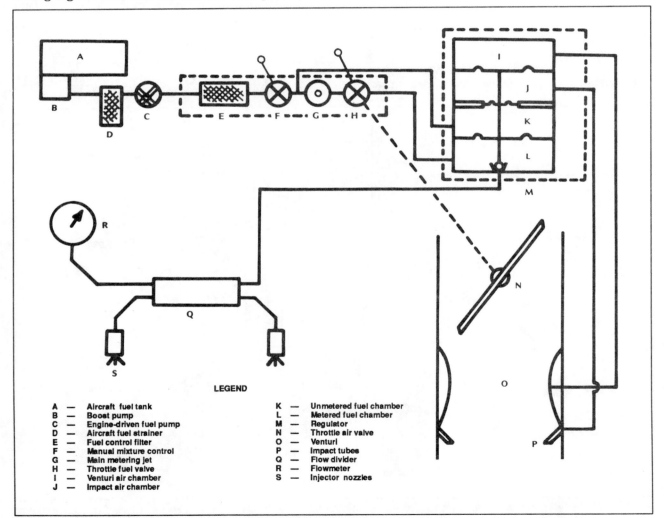

LEGEND

A	—	Aircraft fuel tank	K	—	Unmetered fuel chamber
B	—	Boost pump	L	—	Metered fuel chamber
C	—	Engine-driven fuel pump	M	—	Regulator
D	—	Aircraft fuel strainer	N	—	Throttle air valve
E	—	Fuel control filter	O	—	Venturi
F	—	Manual mixture control	P	—	Impact tubes
G	—	Main metering jet	Q	—	Flow divider
H	—	Throttle fuel valve	R	—	Flowmeter
I	—	Venturi air chamber	S	—	Injector nozzles
J	—	Impact air chamber			

Figure 6-9. Precision Airmotive RSA Fuel Injection System.

5. *What is adjusted to vary the idle fuel-air mixture ratio?*

6. *Would the mixture ratio become richer or leaner if the servo bleed where to become restricted?*

7. *What does the fuel flowrmeter actually measure on this injection system?*

B. Precision Airmotive RSA Fuel Injection Systems

The Precision Airmotive RSA system differs from the RS in that it does not use a servo system to control the flow of operational fuel. The line diagram of Figure 6-9 will help follow the flow in this system.

1. Air Metering Force

The air metering force is similar to that used in the RS system. The impact tubes P, in the inlet of the throttle body, sense the pressure of the air entering the engine and the venturi O senses its velocity. These two forces move the air diaphragm proportional to the amount of air ingested into the engine.

2. Fuel Metering Force

Fuel from the engine driven fuel pump C enters the fuel control through the filter E and the mixture control valve F. Some of this fuel acts on the diaphragm to cause it to close the ball valve. Fuel for the engine operation flows through the main metering jet G and the throttle fuel valve H into chamber L of the regulator M. This metered fuel opens the ball valve.

3. Metered Fuel Flow

The actual metering is done by the pressure drop across the orifices. In this system the metering force is determined by the position of the ball valve in its seat. The inlet pressure is held relatively constant by the engine driven fuel pump and the outlet pressure is controlled by the balance between the fuel and air metering forces. When the throttle is opened, the air metering force increases; this opens the valve and lowers the pressure downstream of the orifices and in chamber L. The pressure in chamber K is greater than that in L, by the drop across the fuel control, and tends to close the valve. The balance between the air and

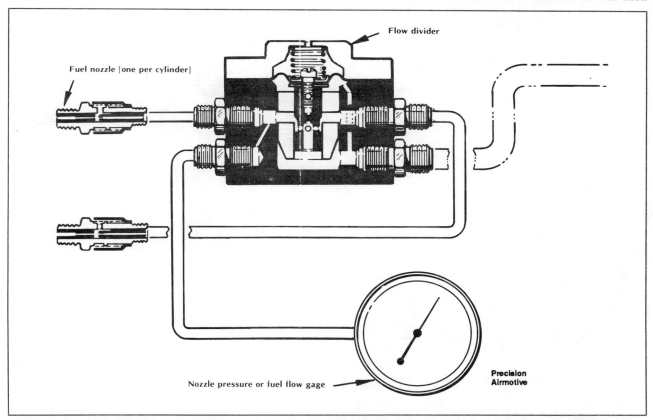

Figure 6-10. *The flow divider, in addition to distributing the fuel evenly to all cylinders, provides a constant pressure for metering until the pressure is sufficient to open the valve completely.*

fuel forces therefore holds the valve off its seat a stabilized amount for any given airflow.

4. Flow Divider

After the fuel leaves the regulator, it flows through a flexible hose to the flow divider, Figure 6-10, located on top of the engine in a central location. The injector nozzles are connected to the flow divider by $^1/_8$" stainless steel tubing. A pressure gauge in the cockpit reads the pressure at the outlet of the flow divider. This is actually the pressure drop across the injector nozzles and is directly

proportional to the fuel flow through the nozzles. For all flow conditions other than idle, the restriction of the nozzles causes a pressure to build up in the metered fuel lines which influences the fuel metering force. Under idle flow conditions, the opposition caused by the nozzles is so small that metering would be erratic. To prevent this, a spring holds the flow divider valve closed to oppose the fuel flow until metered fuel pressure becomes sufficient to off-seat it.

For idle fuel flow, the flow divider opens only partially and thus serves the double function of creating the downstream pressure for the fuel control and dividing the fuel to the cylinders for these extremely low flow conditions. When the mixture control is placed in the Idle Cut-Off position, the flow divider provides cut-off for the fuel.

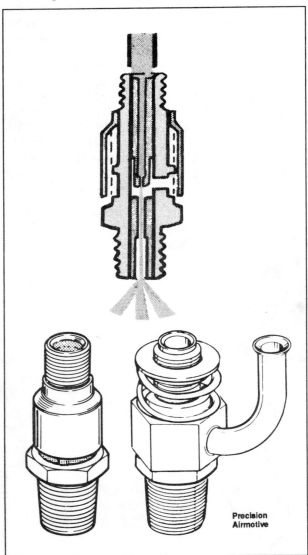

Figure 6-11. *Airbleed nozzles have a calibrated orifice through which the fuel flows and collects in a chamber until the engine intake valve opens. The low pressure draws air through the airbleed, emulsifying the fuel and spraying it out into the intake valve chamber.*

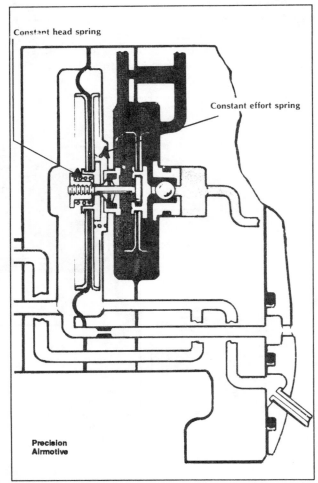

Figure 6-12. *The constant head spring provides a constant fuel pressure for idling, and the constant effort spring aids the diaphragm in moving out of idle into cruise metering.*

5. Injection Nozzles

This system also uses an airbleed type nozzle. These nozzles screw into the cylinder head near the intake port. Each nozzle consists of a brass body which incorporates a metering orifice, an airbleed hole, and an emulsion chamber. Around this body is a fine mesh metal screen and a pressed steel shroud. These nozzles are calibrated to flow within plus or minus 2% of each other and are interchangeable between engines and cylinders. An identification mark is stamped on one of the hex flats of the nozzle opposite the airbleed hole. When installing a nozzle in a horizontal plane, the airbleed hole should be positioned as near the top as practical to minimize fuel bleeding from the opening immediately after engine shut down.

6. Idle System

When there is a low airflow through the engine such as is encountered during idling, the air metering forces are not sufficient to open the ball valve enough for idle fuel to flow. The air diaphragm is between two springs which hold the ball valve off its seat until the airflow becomes sufficient. The constant head spring, Figure 6-12, pushes against the air diaphragm and forces the ball valve off its seat. This maintains a constant head of pressure across the fuel control. As the airflow increases, the air diaphragm moves over, compressing the constant head spring until the diaphragm bushing makes solid contact with the ball valve shaft. Beyond this point the ball valve acts as though it is directly connected to the diaphragm. A smooth transition between idle and cruise RPM is provided by the use of the constant effort spring working between the air diaphragm and the housing. This spring, in effect, preloads the air diaphragm, giving it an initial loaded position from which to work.

As with any fuel metering system, this one controls the idle RPM by limiting the amount of air allowed to flow past the throttle valve, and the idle mixture by the amount of fuel allowed to flow to the discharge nozzles.

A spring loaded screw, Figure 6-13, contacts a stop on the throttle body to limit the amount the throttle air valve can close. An adjustable-length rod connects the throttle air valve to the throttle fuel valve and controls the amount the throttle fuel valve remains open. Adjustment of this length determines the idle mixture ratio, and ultimately the idle manifold pressure.

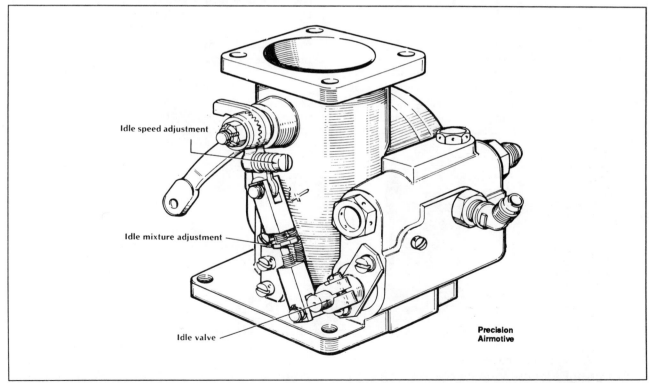

Idle speed adjustment

Idle mixture adjustment

Idle valve

Precision Airmotive

Figure 6-13. Idle RPM is adjusted by the spring-loaded screw which contacts the throttle stop, and the idle mixture ratio by the length of the rod which connects the throttle air valve with the fuel valve.

7. Manual Mixture Control

A spring loaded, flat plate type valve in the fuel control is moved by a linkage from the cockpit to regulate the amount of fuel that can flow to the main metering jet. When the mixture control is placed in the idle cut-off position, the passage to the main metering jet is completely closed and no fuel can flow to the jet. In the full rich position, the opening afforded by the mixture control is larger than the metering jet, and the jet limits the flow. In any intermediate position, the opening is smaller than the main jet and the mixture control becomes the flow limiting device.

8. Automatic Mixture Control

A reverse tapered needle attached to a bellows, Figure 6-14, varies the airbleed between the air chambers of the regulator. The bellows contains helium to sense density changes and a small amount of inert oil to dampen vibrations. As the air density decreases, either from an increase in either altitude or temperature, the pressure inside the bellows causes it to expand. This increases the bleed across the air diaphragm which decreases the air metering force and leans the mixture.

9. Installation And Service

The Precision Airmotive RSA fuel injector mounts on the engine in the location normally occupied by the carburetor, and the flow divider mounts on the crankcase above the cylinders. The injector connects to the flow divider by a flexible line, and the flow divider to the individual nozzles with stainless steel tubing. The fuel flow indicator also connects to the flow divider. The aircraft fuel system required for this injector is quite standard, using a boost pump of either the plunger or centrifugal type to supply pressure to the injector for starting. Fuel flows through the main strainer, through or parallel with an engine driven pump into the main fuel control unit. The inlet fuel pressure is not critical, but must be within the range specified by the airframe manufacturer.

Service required by this injection system is typical for fuel metering systems. The strainer should be cleaned after the first twenty-five hours of operation and every fifty hours after that. All nuts and screws should be checked for security, and the entire installation checked for indication of fuel stain. The throttle and mixture control linkage should be checked for tightness and freedom of operation.

10. Starting Procedure

Engines equipped with this injection system are started by first placing the mixture control in the idle cut-off position and opening the throttle about 1/8 of the way. Turn on the master switch and the boost pump. Move the mixture control to the Full Rich position until there is an indication of flow on the flow meter and return the mixture control to the idle cut-off. Turn the ignition on and engage the starter. As soon as the engine starts, move the mixture control to the Full Rich position.

Fuel injected engines have the reputation of being difficult to start when they are hot. This is largely due to the fact that the high temperatures

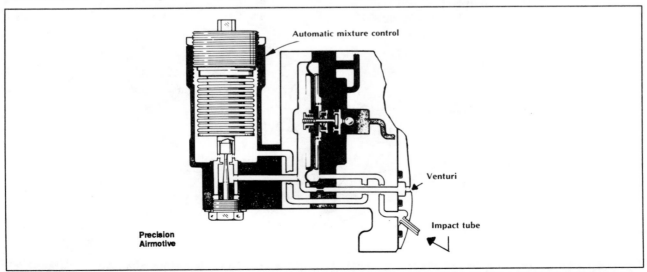

Figure 6-14. The automatic mixture control maintains the mixture ratio as the pilot sets it by controlling the pressure differential across the air diaphragm.

in the engine nacelle cause the fuel in the lines to vaporize and the lines from the flow divider to the nozzles will be full of vapor rather than liquid fuel. The lines must be purged of all vapors before an effective start can be made.

11. Idle Speed And Mixture Adjustment

Before attempting to make any adjustment to the fuel metering system, it must be determined that the engine is operating properly. Both magnetos and all of the spark plugs must be doing their proper job. The engine should develop its rated static RPM and it must have the proper oil or cylinder head temperature.

Turn the airplane across wind and close the throttle to the desired idle speed, usually somewhere around 650 RPM. Slowly and carefully move the mixture control toward the idle cut-off position. Observe the tachometer during the leaning. The RPM should increase approximately 25 to 50 RPM as the mixture control is pulled back. Return the mixture control to Rich before the engine dies. An increase of more than this indicates the mixture is too rich and you should shorten the idle mixture control linkage to increase the fuel flow. This is done by screwing the coarse threads of the adjustment screw into the rod. After making this adjustment, momentarily open the throttle to approximately 2000 RPM to clear the spark plugs of any fouling that may have occurred during idling. If, when the throttle is returned to the idle position, the RPM has changed it must be corrected and a final check made of the mixture before the idle adjustments may be considered completed.

QUESTIONS:

8. Does an increase in the air metering force open or close the ball valve in the regulator of this system?
9. What is the purpose of the airbleed in an injector nozzle?
10. What is adjusted to change the idle fuel-air mixture ratio?
11. What does the automatic mixture control regulate to hold the fuel-air mixture ratio constant with the changes in air density?

Chapter VII
Teledyne-Continental Fuel Injection System

The Continental fuel injection system meters its fuel as a function of the engine RPM, and does not use air flow as a metering force. A special engine driven pump, an integral part of the system, produces the fuel metering pressure.

A. Components

1. Injection Pump

The pump is the heart of this fuel injection system. It is basically a vane type, constant displacement pump with special features that allow it to produce an output pressure which varies with the engine speed. If a passage containing an orifice bypasses the pump mechanism, Figure 7-1, the output pressure will vary according to the speed of the pump and the size of the orifice will determine the pressure for any given speed. If its size is increased, the output pressure will decrease. This system works well for flows in the cruise or high power range, but when the flow is low, as in idling, there is not enough restriction to maintain a constant output pressure. An adjustable pressure relief valve is therefore installed in this line. During idle the output pressure is determined by the setting of the relief valve and the orifice has no effect, while at the high power end of operation, the relief valve is off its seat and the pressure is determined by the orifice.

Any fuel injection system must have vapor free fuel in its metering section, and provision is made in the pump to remove all vapor from the fuel and return it to the tank.

Fuel enters the pump through a chamber where the vapor is swirled out of the liquid and collects in the top. Some fuel from the pump outlet returns to the tank through a venturi arrangement on the top of this chamber and produces a low pressure which attracts the vapors and returns them to the tank.

A final feature in this pump is a by-pass check valve around the pump so fuel from the boost pump may flow to the fuel control for starting. As soon as the engine pump pressure becomes higher

than that of the boost pump, the valve closes and the engine pump takes over.

Turbocharged engines have a unique problem during acceleration. If the fuel flow increases before the turbocharger has time to build up to speed and increase the airflow proportionately, the engine may falter from an overly rich mixture. Pumps for these engines have the simple orifice replaced with a variable restrictor controlled by an aneroid valve. An evacuated bellows is surrounded by upper deck pressure, actually the turbocharger discharge pressure. This bellows moves a valve which controls the size of the orifice, varying the output fuel pressure proportional to the inlet air pressure. When the throttle is opened and the engine speed increases, rather than immediately supplying an increased fuel pressure to the control the aneroid holds the orifice open until the turbocharger speed builds up and increases the air pressure into the engine. As the inlet air pressure increases, the orifice becomes smaller and the fuel pressure, and therefore the flow, increases.

The drive shaft of the pump has a loose coupling to take care of any slight misalignment between the pump and the engine drive.

2. Fuel Control Unit

The line diagram, Figure 7-2, of this system shows the fuel flow from the tank to the cylinders. Fuel flows from the tank A, through the boost pump B, and the aircraft main strainer C into the pump. Fuel leaves the pump with a pressure proportional to the engine speed modified by the turbocharger discharge, or upper deck pressure. It flows through the fuel control filter I, into the manual mixture control valve J. This valve differs from that used by the Precision Airmotive systems, as it acts as a variable selector rather than a shut-off valve. When the mixture is in the cut-off position, all fuel is bypassed back to the tank and none flows to the engine. In the full rich position, all of the fuel flows to the engine. Any intermediate position drops the pressure upstream of the metering orifices by routing some of the fuel back to the tank and some to the engine. A metering

18. What is adjusted by the relief valve setting on the Continental fuel injection pump?

   A. High unmetered fuel pressure.
   B. Low unmetered fuel pressure.
   C. High metered fuel pressure.
   D. Low metered fuel pressure.

19. What is adjusted by the orifice size on the Continental fuel injection pump?

   A. Low unmetered fuel pressure.
   B. Low metered fuel pressure.
   C. High metered fuel pressure.
   D. High unmetered fuel pressure.

20. What does the aneroid valve on a Continental fuel injection pump, used for turbocharged engines, control?

   A. The turbocharger discharge pressure.
   B. Fuel injection system upper deck pressure.
   C. Low unmetered fuel pressure.
   D. The size of the orifice.

Answers To Final Examination

Aircraft Fuel Metering Systems

1.	B	11.	A
2.	C	12.	B
3.	A	13.	C
4.	D	14.	B
5.	A	15.	C
6.	A	16.	D
7.	A	17.	A
8.	B	18.	B
9.	C	19.	D
10.	D	20.	D